RAIN ON THE
PAVEMENTS

Also available from
New London Editions

Scamp
Roland Camberton

RAIN ON THE PAVEMENTS

Roland Camberton

New London Editions

Rain on the Pavements
by Roland Camberton (Henry Cohen)

Published in 2010
by New London Editions

New London Editions 3

New London Editions is an imprint of
Five Leaves Publications
PO Box 8786, Nottingham NG1 9AW
www.fiveleaves.co.uk

ISBN: 978-1-905512-95-9

Rain on the Pavements
was first published in 1951
by John Lehmann Ltd
Cover Illustration by John Minton,
courtesy of Royal Society for the Arts

Typeset by Four Sheets Design and Print
Printed in Great Britain

Five Leaves acknowledges financial support
from Arts Council England

Five Leaves is represented by Turnaround
and distributed to the book trade by Central Books
Five Leaves is a member of the Inpress group
of independent publishers
(www.inpressbooks.co.uk)

CONTENTS

PART ONE
UNCLE YUNKEL

1

AVID'S FIRST and greatest hero was Uncle Yunkel.
He was younger than most uncles; he was, in fact,
nine, at the time when David was three. Even so,
he was older than Auntie Debby, who was six.

The first memory of David's life was of Yunkel clinging
to the back of a lorry, which was racing down Fareland
Avenue, in Dalston. By standing on tiptoe and peering
out of the window, David was just able to observe this
scene, in which he found nothing extraordinary.

Later, when David was six, Yunkel was allowed to take
him out on Sunday afternoons. When they had saved up
sixpence each, enough to buy an all-day ticket on the
trams, the whole of London was at their disposal. They
climbed up the steep stairs of a tram and ran to the front,
where Yunkel immediately took charge.

"Now you just watch, David," he said. "Watch care-
fully." He settled down comfortably, glanced round to see
that everything was in order, and firmly gripped the back
of a seat.

"These are the controls," he said.

He steered the tram with perfect mastery along the
rails. As it approached the next stop, he pulled with all
his strength at the back of the seat. At first the tram
resisted and continued along its course. But gradually
Yunkel's pull on the seat had its effect. The tram, in spite
of itself, felt the iron hand of the young master and
slowed down reluctantly to a halt.

Yunkel smiled a little in unassuming triumph, then frowned in anticipation of his next task, to get the tram going again. He clenched his teeth and pressed down on the controls. Nothing happened until, quite incidentally, a bell clanged on the driver's platform. At that moment, by a superhuman effort, Yunkel got the vehicle to move again. He relentlessly pressed and pulled on the controls and brought the tram to a steady speed. Only then did he relax a little, smiling significantly and guiding the tram on its smooth course along the rails.

He was a dark, curly-headed youngster, not much bigger than David himself, and seemed incredibly handsome. In particular, David was brought to admire his nose.

"Your nose," Yunkel pointed out, "is not straight. Now look at mine. Mine is straight. You could run a ruler along it, couldn't you?"

"Yes," David agreed. He thought — and perhaps said — that in every other respect Yunkel was perfect, too.

"Now your nose," Yunkel continued, "is not bad. I'm not saying that. Of course, it's fairly large, and it's not straight. But I'm not saying it's bad."

In this question of noses, as in many others, David found a sympathetic and good-natured ally in Auntie Debby. She argued the case for their noses with what seemed to him unnecessary vehemence, considering that Yunkel had already laid down the law. Though she always denied that her nose was in the same class as David's, it was clear, nevertheless, that she was speaking for both of them.

"Long noses are better than short noses," she declared. "What's the use of a small nose that you can hardly see? No! Don't be silly of course long noses are better than short noses! Aren't they, David?"

He hesitated. She nudged him and whispered urgently, "Go on! Say yes, you silly!"

"No," he decided, "they're not."

"Oh, he *is* silly!" exclaimed Debby. "Fancy not sticking up for your own side!"

But Debby was not allowed to accompany them very far. Her tastes were in any case entirely different from theirs. Her favourite activity was wheeling prams and playing at "mothers and children". They usually managed to fix her up with a pram in Penderton Road or Dibley Road.

"Just up and down, mind!" said the baby's mother. "You mustn't go past number 28! Just wheel it up and down in front of the gate."

Debby was now quite happy, and they left her to continue their philosophic walks and excursions.

Sunday was their great day. They went everywhere, absolutely everywhere. Had they not tried the most obscure routes, had they gone to the last fare stage, then they would not have been getting their full sixpence-worth. Every destination on the trams which ran through Hackney demanded a pilgrimage. But these were only a beginning. They were the starting-points of new trails, to Hampstead, to Purley, to New Cross, to Wanstead Flats.

Nevertheless, even at this early age, they turned for preference to the West End. One Sunday, David, for one, came to the definite realisation that some kind of selection was necessary. Travelling through the East End — familiar ground — they arrived in Limehouse, and David looked round anxiously and fearfully for Chinamen and murderers. But Yunkel, as usual, was calm and rather disdainful of his nephew's cowardice.

"You mustn't be windy, David," he said. "Be anything you like, but not windy."

To show his assurance, Yunkel whistled, in his own special way, with his lower lip drawn back. To the music of this entirely sophisticated whistle, they entered Blackwall Tunnel. There seemed to be no one else in the tunnel; only an occasional bus rumbled through. Their steps became more forlorn; Yunkel's whistle echoed eerily.

"How long is it?" asked David.

"About a mile," Yunkel replied. "Maybe a quarter of a

mile, I don't know. Anyway, it's the longest tunnel in the world."

A mile, a quarter of a mile, there didn't seem to be much difference. A mile was a long way, you saw it on maps.

"Yunkel," said David, "what about going to Buckingham Palace?"

"You're not windy, are you?"

"No."

"Are you telling me the truth?"

"Well... I admit I'm a bit windy..."

"It doesn't matter really," said Yunkel, "you're only a kid, you're not seven yet. And shall I tell you something, David?" he added, with that frankness and simplicity which made him so human, demi-god though he was, "I'm a bit funky myself."

"It's nicer up there anyway," said David, "round Buckingham Palace."

"Well, what do you expect? That's where all the lords live."

"Like Mr. Framberg," said David, "he's a lord."

"I'm not so sure about that," said Yunkel. "They call him a lord, because he's so posh, but I'm not sure if he's a lord really. He used to ride on a horse, though. He told me himself."

David pictured Mr. Framberg with his neat beard of pure white, his spats, and the grey morning jacket in which he walked with grave dignity through the synagogue. And then he pictured him on a horse, a pure white charger. Nothing, surely, could be more lordly, more regal, in fact.

"Why doesn't Mr. Framberg live round Buckingham Palace then?"

"Because he lives in Penderton Road, of course. Don't forget, Penderton Road is a posh road. Rich people live there. They used to have carriages down there, you ask your mummy, she remembers."

They were continuing, somewhat reluctantly, deeper into the tunnel.

10

"Let's go round Buckingham Palace," David persisted. "Ay? Go on, be a sport."

"All right," Yunkel conceded, "we'll go back then."

They turned back and found their way to the 65 tram route. Yunkel drove with exceptional verve all the way to Holborn. En route, near Farringdon, their road passed over a whole district where the streets lay forty or fifty feet below their level.

"That," said Yunkel, looking up for a moment from the seat-back with which he controlled the bucking, careering tram, "that is the underworld."

The underworld! So *that* was the underworld! So there, thought David, below him, in Clerkenwell, was revealed a section of that mysterious nether universe of which he read in the papers. He tried to catch a glimpse of what was going on in its subterranean streets. But they were quite empty, except for two children playing with a hoop in the middle of the road. Children of the underworld... How much he was learning! How much Yunkel knew! And with what masterly nonchalance Yunkel passed through the strangest and most overwhelming districts in London.

They spent half-an-hour or so watching the trams entering and coming out of Kingsway Tunnel, and then wandered down Kingsway to the Embankment, Yunkel coolly appraising the height of the buildings. David followed his example — it was a change from reading aloud the advertisements on every hoarding in sight. He counted and recounted, to make sure, the number of storeys in an impressive block of offices.

"Look," he said, "there's one eight storeys high."

"That's nothing," said Yunkel composedly, for he was wonderfully tolerant of David's simplicity and undiscriminating enthusiasm, "there's skyscrapers in New York fifty storeys high."

"Do skyscrapers really scrape the sky?" asked David.

"Almost," Yunkel replied. "They're like mountains. At the top you have to have special oxygen to breathe."

"Are they higher than Mount Everest?"

"Not quite. No one has ever climbed Mount Everest."

"Look," said David, "there's Big Ben. That's Uncle Benny's name, Ben."

"That's the exact time," said Yunkel. "no one else in the world's got the time as exact as us. They may only be a minute out, they may only be a second out —"

"Even a fraction of a second?"

"Even a fraction of a second —"

"Can't science make them exact?"

"Not even science can't."

"Only God can," said David.

"You mustn't take God's name in vain," said Yunkel. "God can do anything."

They walked rather guiltily past the policemen outside the Houses of Parliament. Sometimes they kept their eyes averted and sometimes they looked boldly into the policemen's faces to show they had nothing to be afraid of. They hadn't run away from home, they weren't "rough boys". Nevertheless, they knew that policemen could see right through people. Besides, the policemen might mistake them for somebody else.

They paid one of their regular inspection visits to 10 Downing Street, and then followed their usual route to Buckingham Palace. David was beginning to feel tired and wanted to go home.

"Yeh, we'd better go soon," said Yunkel, "your mummy wants you home tea-time. I could stay out late if I wanted to."

"But who'd collect the books?" said David. Yunkel had the enviable job of collecting the prayer-books in the synagogue after evening service. That was only one of the advantages of being the beadle's son. It was true David was allowed to help; but he wasn't permitted to pile them up and lock them away with the special key which Yunkel kept on the end of a chain, along with about twenty others — for heaven alone knows what purposes — in his left-hand trouser pocket. Perhaps, if Yunkel put him on the tram and stayed in the

West End, perhaps he might... But no.

"You're quite right, David," said Yunkel. "I've got to see to my job."

"Is the king a Jew?" said David as they came in sight of the palace.

"No, he's a Christian," said Yunkel. "In Palestine the king'll be a Jew, when the Messiah comes. Rothschild is richer than the king. When the king wants to borrow money, he has to go to Rothschild. Rothschild is the richest man in the world."

"When *will* the Messiah come?" asked David.

"He can come any time," said Yunkel. "He can come tomorrow and he can come in fifty million billion years' time."

David's relentless demand for information extended itself once again to the palace. A perennial question cropped up.

"What does the king do in all those rooms, Yunkel? Does he have one room for eating his breakfast in and one room for eating his dinner in and one room for eating his tea in and one room for when he's being dressed — do you think one room can hold all his suits? Has he got more than a hundred suits?"

"Yeh," said Yunkel, "he's got a special room for everything. He's got more than a thousand suits. He's not allowed to do anything. If he wants to open a book, he has a special servant to open it; and if he wants to turn over the page, then another special servant has to turn it over for him. That's his special job. Each servant's got his special job. There's one man specially to cut his nails, and there's one man specially to comb his hair with a special golden comb."

"Yunkel" — David lowered his voice — "what about the king's bathroom?"

"The king's bathroom alone," said Yunkel, "is bigger than your whole house, and its walls are made of gold."

It was time to go. David was pleasantly tired and cold, knowing well that the kitchen in grandfather's house

13

would be warm and full of aunts and uncles; that his mother would be there, that his father would look in on his way to the synagogue, that a vast, continuous tea would be in progress — probably with pickled herring and fresh "chala" bread that made him want to go on eating for ever — that a crowded, cosy evening lay ahead, between grandfather's house and the synagogue, and that Yunkel would be with him the whole time. Wherever Yunkel was, there was the centre of the world, the centre of significant activity.

As they descended the basement steps to grandfather's kitchen, Yunkel struck up his jaunty whistle, with his lower lip pulled back. This was his light-hearted defiance of the family, so that they could begin saying, before even he had entered the room, "Ah! Yunkel's here already!" Yunkel pushed open the door, advanced into the centre of the kitchen, took off his overcoat, and demanded his indoor jacket.

"Yunkel's tricks!" roared Uncle Harry.

"You were just the same," said David's mother.

"*I* was just the same!" exclaimed Uncle Harry. "At *his* age! At the age of twelve I was a man already."

"Yes," said Auntie Bessie, "and you had your office in the bedroom upstairs. Lord help us if we went into your office to make the bed. I remember! Don't tell me!"

"Rachel," said Yunkel, "get me my indoor jacket." Auntie Rachel, one and a half years his senior, was his main antagonist.

"Jacket!" said Auntie Rachel. "I'll give you jacket!"

Yunkel circled her slowly, giving David meanwhile a wink.

"Harry!" cried Auntie Rachel, "look at him messing about. Tell him to shut up."

Yunkel retreated a little and began to sing in a grotesquely comic nasal voice:

"Rachel! Rachel! Whaddeye think uh that!
A great big fat — uh — lady

Sat upon my hat!
A great big fat — uh — lady
Sat upon my hat!
Rachel, Rachel, Rachel! Whaddeye think uh that!"

Then Yunkel switched off, as it were; he became grave and earnest in quest of tea. As in most families, it was the convention in the Levy-Hirsch households that a man was incapable of getting himself even the simplest meals; was incapable of even fetching a plate, knife, and fork. David's aunts, particularly the younger ones, who were of the modern generation which questioned everything, sometimes disputed the justice of this tradition.

"Haven't you got hands?" they asked. "Are we your slaves?"

"Go on, be a sport," Yunkel urged. "Ay? Go on.... Who's going to get my tea?"

"The tea's on the table in front of you," said Auntie Esther. "There's the bread, there's the butter, there's the herring, there's the tomatoes, the kettle's boiling — what more do you want?"

"Ah, go on," Yunkel wheedled, "get it all ready, pour it out. Who volunteers to get me and David tea?"

In the end, David's aunts relented. They always did, even though they were perhaps on the point of going out or had been serving tea continuously for the last two hours. In the last resort they bowed to immemorial tradition. After all, a man had to go to synagogue, to learn Talmud, to attend or conduct Hebrew classes, to do a host of exclusively masculine things, Yunkel was almost thirteen, he was almost a man.

"Here you are," said Auntie Rosie, handing him a cup of tea, "my lord!"

Meanwhile Auntie Debby, "Baby", the youngest of the family and an angel of quiet industry and altruism, had already cut and buttered a loaf of "chala" bread.

In the corner, a conversation of a quite different order was in progress between Rita Gluckstein and David's

15

elder aunts. Mysterious, arch phrases occasionally reached his ear. "To conceal," he heard Rita say, "is to reveal...."

2

D AVID'S FATHER took Class Three in the Dibley Talmud Torah Hebrew Classes. Class Three was a notoriously tough class, and its most troublesome pupil, as far as David's father was concerned, was Uncle Yunkel. Not that Yunkel was, fundamentally, more of a handful than, say, Solly "Schmalzherring" Cohen or Hymie Katz or the brothers Polinsky or Fatty Levine. The difficulty lay in the relationship between teacher and pupil. Yunkel was Mr. Hirsch's brother-in-law.

The disciplinary measures to be taken in class against a brother-in-law set Mr. Hirsch an unusual pedagogic problem. His solution, when Yunkel became too difficult, was to lock his youthful brother-in-law in the bottom half of a large cupboard in the corner of the classroom. This at least prevented Yunkel from making faces, or at any rate prevented those hideous and irresistible faces from being seen. But it did not prevent Yunkel from whistling or from making a resonant noise in his throat — "Glong!"

However, Yunkel was a sensible lad, and David's father had no wish to push matters to extremes; so when the class had had enough fun from this source, Mr. Hirsch shouted "Yunkel!" in a tone of voice which showed his incipient anger, and there was silence in the cupboard until very near the end of the lesson.

Sometimes Yunkel became so subdued in his cupboard after this authoritative shout, that Mr. Hirsch forgot all about him. David waited for his father in the much-betrampled and quite bare front garden of the Hebrew classes in Dibley Road. Mr. Hirsch, who was tall and walked very fast, came striding out of the front door, when classes were over, and sped away in long, fast steps up Dibley Road. David broke off his desultory game, caught up with his father, and trotted smartly by his side. It was only, perhaps, when they had reached the public-house at the junction of Rutherstone Road and Dibley Road, that David realised something was wrong.

"Dad!" he exclaimed in horror, "where's Yunkel?"

His father's strides wavered, then came to an abrupt halt. They turned round, accelerated, and sped back to the Dibley Talmud Torah Hebrew Classes.

"What do you think of that!" murmured Mr. Hirsch. "He was so quiet today I clean forgot about him."

When the cupboard was opened, Yunkel had ready his most hideous face with which to delight David and demonstrate his unbreakable spirit.

"What a rascal!" Mr. Hirsch exclaimed, with a hint of admiration in his voice, and recognition for a worthy foe.

The whole question of discipline in the Dibley Talmud Torah Hebrew Classes was fraught with insurmountable difficulties. Discipline there had to be. The pupils belonged to a vigorously independent generation of a race which had frequently had to maintain a watchful aware-ness. At this stage of their emancipation, they and their parents were particularly on their guard against anyone taking any damn liberties with them. And that was just what the Hebrew teachers were constantly accused of doing.

If "Stinker" Mandelbaum, for instance, after an hour of maddening insolence, was called a blackguard and a good for nothing by the infuriated Mr. Levitsky, then "Stinker" got up on his hind legs and said, his face crimson with indignation, "I'm not standing for that!"

"Then sit for it!" exclaimed Mr. Levitsky, and pushed him down in his seat again. "Stinker" mumbled some-thing under his breath.

"What was that?" said Mr. Levitsky, whipping round like lightning and trying to surprise "Stinker" into an abject surrender. For a moment or two it was touch and go whether Mr. Levitsky's swift manoeuvre had succeeded or whether the more daring malcontents would back "Stinker" up in creating a minor riot.

In either case, it was fairly certain that "Stinker" Mandelbaum's father would be round the following evening from Ridley Road Market to wave a large raw fist in front of Mr. Levitsky's nose and accuse him of having sullied the Mandelbaum name in an intolerable fashion. At the same time, to show that he was absolutely impartial in his demand for reasonable behaviour on all sides, Mr. Mandelbaum would there and then give young "Stinker" such a clout over the ear as no Hebrew teacher, not even in the toughest classes in Stepney or Bethnal Green, would ever dare let fly at an eleven-year-old head.

What narked him, Mr. Mandelbaum would afterwards explain more conciliatorily to the headmaster, was that he paid half-a-crown a week for his son to come to Hebrew classes, and all his son did was muck about.

That half-a-crown a week narked and cranked a good many parents. It was true they were not absolutely compelled to pay the half-a-crown a week, and if they could not afford it they could get off with one and threepence, or even nothing.

Those who paid only sixpence a week were not the least persistent in harping on the fee. The fact was, it was not so much the money as the principle of the thing. The same argument applied to the fifteen shillings they paid a Cohen after the circumcision ceremony for the redemption of the firstborn; to the money they vowed in the synagogue at their thirteen-year-old son's coming of age; and to various other moneys collected by the beadle. Were these real money, the sort of money Mr. Mandelbaum received when he handed over a piece of fish in Ridley Road Market? Or were they somehow different? Not quite charity, but sums of money handed over with a definite sense of giving?

Mr. Mandelbaum and his group held the latter view, while the Hebrew teachers held the former. David sided very strongly, as was only natural, with the Hebrew teachers, especially when, at the age of thirteen, Yunkel became a private Hebrew teacher. Having just mastered, for his own coming of age, the special sing-song in which the Five Books of Moses had to be chanted, Yunkel was engaged, at a shilling an hour, to coach the son of Yankovitch, the cabinet-maker, for that lad's approaching thirteenth birthday.

It was a great day for uncle and nephew when Yunkel gave his first lesson. Yankovitch, Yunkel, and David met after school one Friday evening. During the winter, Friday was a short day at Dibley Road School; school finished at half-past-two in the afternoon to enable the Jewish boys to make their preparations for the Sabbath, which began at nightfall. By putting on their Sabbath suits, washing their faces, and cleaning their shoes during the lunch-hour, all three were able to give their undistracted attention to the approaching lesson. Yankovitch and Yunkel, who were in the Big Boys', waited for David to come out of the Infants'. Then they walked gravely to Yankovitch's house, feeling that this was a memorable and significant moment in their lives. For Yankovitch this moment was significant because he was going to learn how to sing his portion of the bible. For Yunkel it was significant because he was entering the family profession of Hebrew teacher and religious mentor. As for David, he was Yunkel's nephew and disciple, inevitably associated with his uncle's enterprises.

They arrived at Yankovitch's house in Buckleford Lane.

"You wait here, David," said Yunkel.

David waited at the gate for an hour, looking proudly this way and that. If anyone had come up to him and asked him what he was doing, he would have had no hesitation in telling them. "I am waiting for my uncle, Yunkel Levy, who is inside giving a Hebrew lesson to Mr. Yankovitch's son."

For Yunkel and David, Hebrew teaching was in the family, it was in their blood. David's grandfather took the top class in the Dibley Talmud Torah Hebrew Classes. His father took Class Three. His future uncle Aaron, who was to marry Auntie Bessie, took Class Five. His uncle Harry was already the head of some Hebrew classes in Stepney. His uncle Solly, his uncle Isaac, his uncle Harry's brothers-in-law… And now Yunkel, too, was a man. He was a Hebrew teacher in his own right. No longer could he be locked in cupboards for misbehaviour. Now he could deal out his own punishments…

When Yunkel came out of Yankovitch's house, he did not swank or start flashing his shilling around. He behaved as though nothing had happened. There was a tin lying on the pavement. He kicked it along expertly down into Rutherstone Road. He gave David a pass occasionally, and David shot it back as best he could. He whistled in his special way and went "glong" in his throat. Only when they got near to Polonsky's sweet shop did he open his fist. He did not say anything, there was no need to say anything. "Facts and not words" was Yunkel's frequent exhortation; and there, in his palm, lay a fact, an undeniable, incontrovertible shilling.

"I'll give you your share now," said Yunkel.

They went into Polonsky's shop.

"A ha'pennyworth of sweets for David, Mr. Polonsky," said Yunkel. "Let him choose anything he likes."

3

WHEN ENOUGH shillings had been saved up, Yunkel bought himself a trilby hat, since it was, after all, scarcely becoming for a teacher to visit his pupils wearing a school cap. It did, in fact, seem scarcely proper that Yunkel should go to school at all. Nevertheless, an absurd convention which required men of Yunkel's age to go to school till they were fourteen was yet to inflict upon him some humiliating experiences.

Yunkel's master in Dibley Road School was named Abrahams, of which the natural abbreviation was Abie. That a master in school — not in Hebrew classes or synagogue or anything like that — but in school, a real school, a proper L.C.C. school, should be named Abrahams, Abie for short, was more than Yunkel could bear. So when Mr. Abrahams was taking playtime supervision and walking about the asphalt playground peacefully smoking a cigarette, Yunkel walked past with a couple of other boys and said in a loud voice:

"...and so of course there was my cousin Abie with my uncle Abie eating lokshun soup, when my uncle Abie said to my cousin Abie..."

The first half-a-dozen times or so, Mr. Abrahams probably did not distinguish this scrap of conversation from the rest of the shouting and yelling which made a Dibley Road playtime audible from Penderton Station to Homerton Junction. But after a few weeks, Yunkel's insistence on the word Abie began visibly to annoy him. One day it would be:

"...and so what did Abie say? He said, listen Chatzkel, my name's Abie, not Chatzkel, so if you're talking to me, you're talking to Abie, I'll have you know..."

And another day:

"...so his mother said, Abie! Abie! What's the matter with you, Abie? Can't you hear I'm calling you, Abie?..."

After showing extraordinary patience, Mr. Abrahams at last ordered Yunkel to go and fetch the Cane and Book.

"What for, sir?" said Yunkel, puzzled and innocent.

"For cheek."

"Cheek, sir?" said Yunkel, truly bewildered and uncomprehending.

"Yes, cheek and impudence."

"Cheek and impudence, sir?"

"Levy!" boomed Mr. Abrahams. He was a large man with a powerful voice, the full strength of which he rarely used. Knowing its thunderous volume, he normally spoke with deliberate and restrained gentleness. Now he opened it full throttle. Sniggers and titters died out.

"Levy!" he roared. "Go and fetch the Cane and Book, for cheek, impudence, and impertinence!"

All eyes were turned on Yunkel, who had his lower lip drawn back as though to give his special whistle. Perhaps a slight, thin music did actually emerge from behind his teeth, for Yunkel's whistle was an act of faith, which never deserted him.

Nevertheless, the Cane and Book was a serious affair. There were two sorts of canes in Dibley Road School. There were the canes that masters kept in their desks, personal canes, almost frivolous canes, for summary punishment. Then there was the Cane which lay with the Book in a drawer of the long table beside the headmaster's rostrum in the Big Boys' hall. This was a stout cane, with grey tones and brown knobbly bits. It gleamed dully through long use. Anyone who was whacked with the big Cane had his name inscribed in the Book which always accompanied it.

Mr. Abrahams now wrote in the Book: "J. Levy. Six strokes for impertinence." And Yunkel received "six of the best on the bum".

From time to time, the offence and the punishment were repeated, until the whole process was brought to an end by Yunkel's reaching the age of fourteen, leaving Dibley Road School, and entering the Yeshiva Talmudical College, in the East End, as a day student.

4

DAVID WAS a thin and weakly child and offered warm hospitality to the bacilli of all the infant diseases: measles, German measles, chicken-pox, mumps, and so on. He spent a great many interesting afternoons in the outpatients' departments of the local hospitals, the German Hospital in Dalston Lane, the Metropolitan Hospital in Kingsland Road, and above all, the Children's Hospital in Hackney Road. In their shady gloom, he slid, jumped, and crawled on the floor with other ailing infants, read comics, and had a cup of tea, while his mother compared notes with other mothers, many of whom, after a few years of this routine, she got to know very well indeed, and looked out for in any new out-patients' department to which she was directed.

After a few particularly interesting sessions in the Great Ormond Street Hospital, he had his tonsils out and became thinner than ever. Mrs. Hirsch and David then shifted their attentions to the Jewish Board of Guardians in Middlesex Street. Their afternoon visits to Middlesex Street, the official name of "Petticoat Lane" — or just "the Lane" — were wholly delightful; because when the interviews and examinations at the Board of Guardians were over, they went down the Lane to Rodvin's restaurant to have tea. On the way, they looked in at Bielkofsky's tailor shop, where they opened negotiations which were to lead, after two or three months' hard bargaining, trial, and selection, to David's having a new suit. The suit, it was stipulated, had to be about two sizes too large, so as to give him room in which to grow. At the same time, it was not to be so large as to look like a sack. Also, it had to be of the best quality, the smartest cut, the most reliable workmanship, and the lowest price, as well as having an extra pair of pants. Bielkofsky would, they knew, agree to their terms in the end — not that he wasn't making plenty, the robber! It was well known in their family that Bielkofsky stank with money. Hadn't he been making suits for Yunkel, Solly, and Harry for years?

Well, that was that. Now for a nice cup of tea at Rodvin's. They went upstairs to the first floor and sat by the window overlooking the Lane. Down in that narrow, bubbling torrent, the shop windows shone and sweated, the flares hissed, the hoarse cries tore the air; while upstairs, his mouth watering, David persuaded his mother to buy still more of those delicious chocolate éclairs.

The result of their journey to the Lane was not only a new suit, but also an agreement whereby, for seven and six a week, David was fixed up to spend six months in the Jewish Board of Guardians' Convalescent Home at Broadstairs.

He cried about this, partly out of habit, partly because he did not like the idea of going to "a home". There was not only the social wrench of leaving his parents and his aunts and uncles; there was also the spiritual wrench, of abandoning the heroic life which he led at Yunkel's side. But in any case, he was always ready, as his father put it, "to turn on the water taps".

The home, at Broadstairs, consisted of a large house and a field. He was constrained to sleep in the dormitory by night and to play in the recreation room when it rained. The rest of the time he spent largely in his hut in the far corner of the field. It was a primitive hut made of straw and twigs and built in the hedge, but it suited David and the two companions with whom he shared it very well. Once inside, they flung a camouflage of twigs, grass, straw, and earth over the entrance, fetched out their water bottles and sweets, and prepared for a long siege. The enemy was Miss Pressman, who took them for walks and gave them an hour's lesson each morning, and Nurse Elsie or Nurse Doris, who called them in for meals.

"We're safe here," David said to Jack and Phil, his comrades in the maquis. Yet, oddly enough, the enemy, instead of hunting for them in vain round the field, came straight to their corner of the hedge, flung aside their elaborate camouflage, and said sternly, "Come along, you three!"

However, it was a fine summer, and in spite of the long hours spent in his damp and dirty dug-out, David filled out, gained weight and colour, and enjoyed himself immensely. The walks on the beach and along the seafront began even to seem more interesting than crouching under the hedge. They passed Charles Dickens's house, and David was stimulated to read *Oliver Twist,* which made him regret that London was not still as slummy as in Dickens's day; he already had a perverse fondness for cul-de-sacs in Hoxton with the washing hanging across them, for narrow, dirty alley-ways in Islington where crowds of tattered children rolled and yelled on the paving-stones, and above all for the bright, cosy, pulsating courtyards and backstreets off Whitechapel and Commercial Road.

On the seashore, David and his companions collected shells, ran away in terror from crabs and lobsters, and explored caves, which were all smugglers' caves and still in use. They did not see any smugglers, except for the rough-looking men who messed around with the boats by the jetty — but they did once get cut off by the tide. They retreated further and further into a little bay which lay in the direction of Margate. Things looked pretty serious, because not only were they not sure how far the tide advanced, and whether, in fact, they were going to be drowned; but also because they were going to be late for lunch, and matron was a stickler for punctuality. Fortunately, a scouting party discovered a cave — and not even the most sceptical could deny that *this* was a smugglers' cave — with steps at the back hewn out of the cliff and leading up to the front.

Only one untoward event marred his six months' convalescence in Broadstairs. He unaccountably got conjunctivitis, severe inflammation of the eye, thereby adding another to the formidable list of minor ailments to which his body showed itself so hospitable in these early years. He was shut up in a dark room for a few weeks, with nothing to do except draw the blinds surreptitiously in the evening and spy on the girls' dormitory. Conjunctivitis apart, his health improved enormously, and he began to grow fat. From the age of eight onwards, he was therefore no longer a skinny little boy tagging along behind Yunkel and later heroes, but a big fat boy towering over his heroes in diffuse adiposity and listening open-mouthed to the details of their small, compact, determined assaults upon things in general.

5

WHEN DAVID came back from Broadstairs, everything was changed. Of course. He had changed and other people had changed; it was change squared, so to speak.

Yunkel was now an all-day student at the Yeshiva Talmudical College in Carr Lane, which lay between Commercial Road and Whitechapel in the heart of the East End. He almost always wore a trilby hat, only using his school cap when he wanted to travel at children's rates on the buses. He was fourteen, and there were the beginnings of a moustache on his upper lip. He was — David could already sense it — less inclined to have his nephew as constant companion. He went around with boys of his own age, with Kitzlavski and Malkus. Sometimes he was decidedly reticent. No doubt he considered David childish...

Once or twice he spoke to David about girls.

"Do you know, David," he said, "that it's possible to go out with girls?"

"You mean big girls," said David, "like ladies."

"Yes," said Yunkel.

"Do you like girls?" asked David.

"No," said Yunkel, "they're silly. You have to pay to take them to the pictures, you know. Besides, a religious fellow doesn't go out with girls till he gets engaged."

But David discovered that Yunkel was not so immune from girls as he claimed to be. David was sitting in the corner of his grandfather's kitchen, reading the *Magnet* and keeping his ear cocked for any informative remarks of his elders that might be worth ruminating, when he heard his aunts close in for a combined assault on Yunkel.

"Yunkel, haven't you got any girl friends?" said Auntie Bessie, as she handed him his tea.

"Yes," said Auntie Rosie, "what about it, Yunkel? Come on, no secrets from your sisters!"

"Huh!" snorted Yunkel. "Girls! What do you think I am? I see too much of them at home."

"Well I like that!" said Auntie Bessie. "After I've just given him tea an' all!"

"Isn't there just one girl?" said Auntie Rachel, who was very shrewd and penetrating in her analysis of motives, "not just one girl out of the whole world?"

David followed up this theme of one girl in a private conference with Yunkel in his room, which — like his brother Harry before him — he insisted on calling his office. It was an attic room at the top of the house, and contained only an iron bed, a bare table, a wonky chair, and a shelf nailed to the wall. But on the door there was a large notice inked in with great care:

JACOB LEVY
OFFICE
Do Not Enter

Yunkel's account book stood always in the exact centre of the table, with a pen ranged on one side and a pencil on the other, and a bottle of ink at the head of the account book completing the exact symmetry of the lay-out. In the account book, every halfpenny was methodically accounted for. Thus: "Fares, 2½d. Pickled cucumber, ½d. Bet with Malkus, 1d." Yunkel knew precisely where he stood. "Total assets, week ending 22nd November, 1927 (Christian Era) — 12th Kislev, 5688 (Jewish Reckoning) — 6s. 4½d. Proposed expenditure, 8s. 9d. for a pair of shoes, 4d. for the pictures Tuesday evening. Shoes will have to wait until next week, unless N. will lend me 4s.?"

It was to Yunkel's room, the innermost shrine, that they had retired from the kitchen. Yunkel pulled a fag-end from his pocket.

"Yunkel!" breathed David, in a thrill of horror and admiration.

"It's all right," said Yunkel. "You keep watch at the door just in case grandfather comes up."

"Grandfather's in the front room having a snooze," said David.

"I know. It's quite safe," said Yunkel. Lighting the tiny cigarette's end, he screwed up his face as though to sneeze, and then, with an expansive gesture, blew out smoke and was ready to talk.

"Yunkel," said David, "is it true what they were talking about downstairs, about you liking a girl?"

"It's possible," said Yunkel. "Nothing is impossible."

"Then who is it?" David asked.

"I wouldn't tell even you, David," he said. "I wouldn't tell my own mother, if she was alive. That's something that's private. Everybody's got something that's private. Haven't you?"

"I would tell you anything, Yunkel," said David, "anything you asked. Honest I would."

"Well, which girl do you like, then?" asked Yunkel.

"no one special," said David. "There was only Phyllis in Springfield Park, when I was two. I don't remember that, but my mummy told me about it."

"Of course, you're too young," reflected Yunkel. "But I'll give you a clue," he added. "She's someone you know."

David was off from the mark like a greyhound.

"Rita Gluckstein," he said.

Yunkel was silent, and David respected his silence. Never again did David refer to the subject. But he was glad. Yunkel deserved the best, and Rita Gluckstein was a smart, refined young lady — he had heard her say so herself. She was also — what was the word she was so fond of using? — sophisticated. A perfect match for Yunkel, who was already, as he put it, a man-about-town, catching buses, buying a season ticket from Dalston Junction to Broad Street, having announcements of films sent to him from as far away as the Trocadero, Elephant and Castle.

It was true that no sign of Yunkel's special feeling for Rita ever showed itself. Rita was often in grandfather's kitchen, either talking openly and sophisticatedly about the latest West End plays and Hollywood film stars; or else drawing David's aunts into a huddle about her armchair and saying something which caused them to disperse with shrieks of shocked laughter and incredulous horror. To his childish and quite disinterested eye, Rita's salient feature was her legs. Perhaps this was due to the still fairly ground-level view he had of people at the age of eight. Yet thinking back to his grandfather's animated kitchen, even later, from a height of six feet, he found that Rita's legs were very long and preternaturally visible and ubiquitous. Great lengths of silk-stockinged leg issued forth, like pink ectoplasm, from the armchair in which Rita liked to sit. They hit David in the eye; there was no denying them. They were Rita's legs.

Yunkel, however, did not so much as glance at Rita. It was as much as she could do to get him to answer her. David might almost have thought Yunkel hated her, so abrupt was he and so lacking in his usual playful good-humour. Rita, for her part, treated Yunkel as a joke, a "scream", as he was described in the family circle; for was he not always ready with a laugh, a whistle, a "glong"?

The trouble was that Rita was eighteen and Yunkel was fourteen. Also he was one of the students of the Yeshiva Talmudical College, that band of gay, but poor upholders of religious learning. They were recommended by the elders of the synagogue, but were not to be seriously considered by a smart and refined young lady who had a job in the West End, who went already to Mizrachi dances in Stamford Hill, who was thinking of learning French in night-school.... Alas for David's hopes of a match between Yunkel and Rita! Nothing ever came of them. For years Yunkel buried his nose in the newspaper whenever Rita came into the room. After a time, Rita forgot even to tease him.

6

THE Yeshiva Talmudical College was a red-brick building, only as yet half-blackened by London soot, and neighboured on one side by a Salvation Army Hostel and on the other by a grocer's shop where the students bought pickled cucumbers — "wallies" — during break, or "brek". It was situated off Commercial Road in a district of massive tenements, one street of which was named Rose and Honeydew Street — a cousin of Paradise Row, in Bethnal Green. This particular Yeshiva was built, David was told by his mother, largely as a result of his grandfather's urgent representations to wealthy and religious Jews that London, largest city in the world, should have more than the one Talmudical College which had served it hitherto.

When he arrived at the Yeshiva, the young student found that the Talmud was a commentary on the Old

Testament in thirty or so immense volumes. The commentary itself occupied the centre of the page, while the surrounding space was filled with four or five commentaries upon the commentary in smaller type. At the back of each volume there existed further commentaries in still smaller type. Besides the main volumes, there were subsidiary volumes and literature. The evening students at the Yeshiva had to master the first two or three volumes; the all-day students penetrated further and into more volumes. In addition, there were prayers, three times a day, meals, three times a day, and "brek", twice a day, the last given over to the traditional Yeshiva game of wall-ey, played in the yard against the wall of a neighbouring factory.

At the age of thirteen, Yunkel was transferred from the Dibley Talmud Torah Evening Classes to those of the Yeshiva. The latter, if more arduous, were also more interesting. Not only was the work itself more subtle, offering the enthusiastic student opportunity for legitimate and quite heated disputes with the rabbis; but also there was the travelling to and fro between Hackney and the East End — the journey could be made in at least twelve different ways — and the varied new friends and acquaintances to be made at the Yeshiva, some of whom came from as far afield as Thornton Heath and others from as near as Black Line Yard, the Lane, and Rose and Honeydew Street.

A year later, Yunkel became an all-day student. For reasons of amour-propre as well as economy, he bought a season ticket from Dalston Junction to Broad Street. Wearing his trilby hat, nonchalantly showing his season ticket, and carrying under his arm an evening newspaper, he was already a man-about-town. At the same time, the season ticket entitled him to travel whenever and as often as he pleased between Dalston Junction and Broad Street. So if he had nothing special to do during the holidays, then why not a trip up to Broad Street and back? Or if he were thinking of going to Hampstead Heath for the afternoon, then why not go up to Broad

31

Street and back and *then* catch the Hampstead train from Dalston Junction? Likewise, on the last few occasions when they bought sixpenny all-day tickets on the trams, David had to meet Yunkel at Broad Street. Broad Street became Yunkel's point of universal departure.

Advancing years — fifteen, sixteen, seventeen — naturally brought an increased sense of responsibility. Yunkel, always grave in outward manner, became more deeply preoccupied with his religious studies and Hebrew teaching.

The Broad Street affair was a pointer. Yunkel looked at London with the eyes of a traveller emerging, season ticket in hand, from Broad Street Station. No longer did he begin their joint multi-directional voyages simply and childishly from the Hackney tram-stops. And when he came down the steps of the station — two at a time now, instead of four, an unusual number on which he had prided himself — he was probably in the company of Kitzlavski, Malkus, and even Mendel Blumenstein, who was getting on for twenty. What was David, a shnip of nine or ten, to say to such people?

The falling away in their special relationship became definite and complete with the foundation and rapid collapse of the Dibley Jewish Circle (Youth Section), of which Yunkel was the president, treasurer, and leading spirit. The Dibley Jewish Circle itself was a little junta of adults who belaboured the problems of synagogue, Jewish, and world politics in a basement in Penderton Road. Far-ranging and vehement the discussions always were. But no question was debated more keenly than the constitution of the Circle and its procedure. A chairman was clearly necessary, and two vice-chairmen; a secretary and a treasurer and their deputies. But was a president absolutely essential, and, if so, how many vice-presidents ought there to be? And were there enough members to fill all these posts, while at the same time leaving one or two people as nominal rank and file?

These matters occupied the attention of the adults. In

the Dibley Jewish Circle (Youth Section), which met in Brenton Street — that is to say, *in* Brenton Street, alongside the wall of the corner house — in this youth section, procedure was much simpler. Yunkel was the boss. It was Yunkel's club.

In his opening address Yunkel emphasised this point. It was late one Thursday evening, and he had rushed down specially from the Yeshiva Talmudical College to catch some of the older boys as they came out of the Dibley Talmud Torah Hebrew Classes. Kitzlavski was with him, holding in his hand a notebook and a pencil.

"Come round Brenton Street, anyone who wants to," said Yunkel, waving his arm. "Come on, follow me!"

"Now," said Yunkel, when a crowd of boys had settled their backs against the high, windowless wall of the corner house, "I'll tell you one thing right from the start. This is my club. Anyone who doesn't want to needn't join. Anyone who wants to can join, if he obeys the rules —"

"What are the rules, Yunkel?" interjected Bertie Mackson, less out of any desire to be obstructive than to show that he was following closely, for he was almost as devoted an admirer of Yunkel as David himself.

"The rules," said Yunkel, "are that you pay your subscription, a penny a week for those over eleven, a halfpenny a week for those under, and when we have enough money we go for an outing to Epping Forest —"

"Why not Hampstead Heath?" shouted Solly "Schmalzherring" Cohen.

"Or Hampstead Heath —"

"Richmond is much better! Gah! I've been there!" someone else shouted.

"Kew Gardens!"

"Surrey! Round Boxhill —"

"Listen!" yelled Yunkel. "What have I told you? This is my club, you understand? If you don't shut this row, we pack the whole thing up. Ay, Kitzie?"

Kitslavski nodded. At that moment, the long-suffering

Mrs. Goldstein, who lived in the corner house, leaned over from the front steps and called out: "Why don't you boys go away? What do you think this is, a playground? There's people living here! I'll tell your father, Yunkel Levy, you see if I don't!"

Mrs. Goldstein had a great deal to put up with on account of the vast, high wall of the corner house which backed so conveniently on to Brenton Street. It was known throughout Dalston, Hackney, Stoke Newington, Dibley, and Clapton as positively the best wall on which to play wall-ey. It was so high and so broad, and it was windowless. The continual thump of balls against her kitchen and bedroom drove Mrs. Goldstein to distraction. She fought an energetic, though losing battle with the hordes of purposeful urchins who came, holding tennis balls, rubber balls, discarded golf balls, and even cork balls, to shatter the quiet gloom of Brenton Street and play on her wall. By threats and appeals to parents, she was able to thin out the volley of local balls; but even so, late on summer evenings, lads whom no one knew, who jeered at her menaces, found their way to peaceful Brenton Street and remorselessly pounded her wall with balls and, apparently, bricks.

The meeting beneath her wall of the Dibley Jewish Circle (Youth Section) was a new source of annoyance.

"Sssh," hissed Yunkel fiercely and urgently, "it's Mrs. Goldstein.... It's all right, Mrs. Goldstein!" he called out in tones of smooth diplomacy. "I'll keep them quiet. I'll see to that — If anyone makes a row," continued Yunkel, turning to the crowd of boys, "Mrs. Goldstein'll tell his father. Do you understand, all of yous? All right then ..."

Mrs. Goldstein, after looking at them fixedly for a few moments, went inside her bombarded and beleaguered house. Her appearance, disappearance, and possible reappearance were routine affairs. The nascent Youth Section continued its discussion.

In due course, Yunkel was elected president, treasurer (the key post, that) and assistant secretary. His organising genius and tenacity were such that no less than one-third of the founder members were compelled to fork up and become active, subscribing members. David was one of that third, and handed over his halfpenny a week with enthusiasm. And then, when the time came to go on the first outing to High Beech, his mother refused to let him go....

It was absurd, as he pointed out in the course of eight hours' nagging and lamentation on the preceding Saturday. It was unjust, he added — not in so many words, but in ten thousand times their number — it was humiliating. But nothing could make his mother budge. *He could not go.* Was that clear ? He was too young to go so far, and into the open country, in the company of such a grown-up gang of boys. Yunkel would be too busy to look after him properly; and he had just returned from the convalescent home and must not get caught in the rain and roll about on the damp grass.

David had to report all this to Yunkel. Yunkel was frankly impatient. Many other members had backed out at the last moment and were asking for their subscriptions back. He saw himself going to High Beech only with Kitzlavski, Bertie Mackson, and one or two co-opted members from the Yeshiva. The Dibley Jewish Circle (Youth Section) was fizzling out before it had ever got going. What was more, there was no apparent reason, except the wilful malice of its members, why it should have flopped so disgustingly. The trip to High Beech was a perfectly good idea, a fine, an excellent idea, of aesthetic, educational, and recreational value, and beneficial to the health, and cheap. A change from the Dibley Fields and Brenton Street and playing marbles and "glarneys" in Dibley Road. It was not as if he hadn't collected 5s. 4d. in subscription money after six weeks of pestering and bludgeoning. It was not as if — But, ach! The Jews had been called a stiff-necked people, and stiff-necked they were! An impossible, obstinate, obstructive, uncooperative people...

Those were Yunkel's feelings. As for David, Yunkel was not very concerned about his defection, merely impatient with his pleas to be considered for any future outing and with his improper apologies. David was, after all, a kid. It was up to him to recognise the fact. The trouble lay, not in his backing out, but in his ever having been included in the first place. Yunkel did not disagree with Mrs. Hirsch's objections, but on the contrary, upheld them all too strongly.

The expiry of the Dibley Jewish Circle (Youth Section), the High Beech fiasco, and David's ignominious failure to make the grade were final indications of how he and Yunkel were diverging — reluctantly to be sure, but inevitably.

7

QUITE SUDDENLY David began to see very little of Yunkel, who for five or six years was an all-day student at the Yeshiva Talmudical College. Later, when Yunkel had gone away, and David tried to recall the latter part of that period, he could remember very little. He must, of course, have spent some moments with Yunkel at least once or twice a week, but the memories of those meetings were bare. A few scenes only remained in his mind. There was Yunkel sitting in the corner of the front row of the Perceval Street Synagogue. To the left of him, in diminishing sizes, were the boys of the neighbourhood, whom he hushed occasionally into silence or, more rarely, united in the singing of some traditional tune. Somewhere well down the row, David and his friend Philip held quite undistinguished places.

Or there was a family gathering. Into the crowded, tiny room, rather late, came Yunkel. Behind him loomed the bulky forms of his Yeshiva friends, Kitzlavski, Malkus, and Mendel Blumenstein. They went into a huddle with David's younger married uncles and began some noisy talmudical argument. Then they left early, amid the teasing remonstrances of David's aunts, to go to a meeting. There was always a meeting, a social, a talmudical session which called them away.

Joy of the Law Night, the gayest night in the Jewish year. The Chassidim, that irrepressible sect, held the wildest parties. They danced round the synagogue dais, carrying the Scrolls of the Law, until after midnight. Everyone who was in the know went to the Priznan Rabbi, Rabbi Priznanski, in Upper Newnham Road. When the Hirsches arrived after supper, Yunkel's face was already covered with sweat as a result of his exertions. He and Kitzlavski and Mendel Blumenstein and two or three bearded Chassidim formed the staunch centre of a crowd of dancers who refused to stop, who went on and on and round and round the synagogue dais, singing until they were hoarse. Outside the marquee, specially erected for these celebrations in Rabbi Priznanski's garden, little groups of boys and girls were singing some of the new Zionist songs, dancing the "Horah" dance, or strolling quietly among the pathways. Joy of the Law Night reached a climax when the Chassidim from within the marquee, holding aloft the Scrolls of the Law, marched into Rabbi Priznanski's house and sat down to their long-awaited supper. Yunkel, who had a fine tenor voice and had been giving himself lessons in music, was asked to sing — "but something with a taste!" He sang "Peace be with you, Jew" and "Zion, my beloved". Everyone stopped talking and concentrated on the pickled herring, while Yunkel concluded:

"I shall not find thee, Zion,
I shall not find thee, my beloved ..."

There was a round of applause, and Rabbi Priznanski himself offered Yunkel a glass of Palestinian wine.

Last memory of all. It was three weeks before Yunkel left for Poland, a Sunday afternoon, and they had all smartened themselves up to catch the fifty-three tram for the East End, where the annual (though not unfailingly annual) prizegiving of the Yeshiva Talmudical College was taking place. David himself, an evening student at this time, was to receive a third prize. Yunkel, however, was a top-ranker, a star of the college, and was rehearsing the speech which he had to deliver. On top of the tram, in one of their old front seats, Yunkel said to David, "Ah, the good old East End!"

David wondered what he was driving at. "You sorry to be leaving, Yunkel?" he said.

"I've got to learn this speech," said Yunkel, plunging desperately into the Yiddish script of his notes. "I'll tell you afterwards...."

The tram whined along through Cambridge Heath and Bethnal Green. Yunkel looked up once again.

"Good old Bethnal Green!" he said.

In Whitechapel, it was the same thing.

"Whitechapel!" he said. "Vitechapel! ... Ach! Vitechapel!" He clucked appreciatively.

And yet Yunkel was anxious to go. Grandfather had suggested the idea, but Yunkel needed no persuading. The Carr Lane Yeshiva did not cater for the highest branches of talmudical learning. The obscurer volumes of the Talmud and other esoteric religious matters were studied only in the ancient Yeshivas of Poland. It was to one of these, the Dernov Yeshiva Talmudical College, that Yunkel set out some four years before the outbreak of war. Alas! he never came back.

He was supposed to have stayed five years; but in the fifth year, the Germans advanced on Dernov. He retreated to the Russian lines, perhaps. And then something went wrong. He got lost, in the war, in Russia, in all that tremendous chaos. And after the war, he had still not returned. But somewhere, David was sure, he was remembering — with difficulty, no doubt, because so much had happened — but he was remembering. One day everything would come back to him — why, of course! Hackney! Bethnal Green! Vitechapel! And he would find his way to the old places. They were not themselves without him.

PART TWO
DIBLEY ROAD

1

ON FRIDAY afternoons in winter, there used to sound across the Dibley Fields a full-throated, sextuple cry, capped by a massive roar — D-I-B-L-E-Y — DIBLEY! It was the call of Dibley Road School. On the cinder pitch the Dibleyans were playing football, netball, and handball with neighbouring schools, and if shouting could have won the game, they would rarely have lost.

Dibley was the old school, the family school. David's mother went there, his aunts, his uncles, his cousins; David went there, his younger sisters, his younger brother.

At the age of seven he moved up from the Infants' into the Big Boys', and after a year and a half found himself in Mr. Essand's class. Mr. Essand had a mellow, epicurean philosophy, and the class shared the benefits of its sunny urbanity. The first hour or two of the day was devoted, as was only proper, to work. After work, pleasure.

"Rosenheim," said Mr. Essand.

Desks were tidied, just a single exercise book being left open in case the headmaster or an L.C.C. inspector should come in, and the boys' tongues hung out in eager anticipation of a further thrilling instalment of one of Rosenheim's yarns, retold from the *Champion*. Rosenheim, who was later to do well as a crooner with Dixie Gershbaum's band, put a chair in front of the class and began:

"Well, so they came round the track, throttles open, engines roaring full blast. They came round the speedway almost touching one another — almost touching they were! — racing, racing, closer and closer and closer.

'Get out of my way!' Spiker Scarlet yelled into Jimmie's ear. "Get out of my way, or I'll do you!'"

"Really," murmured Mr. Essand.

Bernstein was now gripped by his story and could not stop. He paid no attention to Mr. Essand's blasé comments, though a few monitors and sycophants near the master's desk tittered a little out of respect.

Mr. Essand lolled back in his chair, sucking sweets. Fresh supplies did not come in till the afternoon, but even in the morning he had a few toffees and lollipops left over from the previous day's collection. After lunch, of course, he would be overloaded with confectionery. Most of the boys bought a half-pennyworth or so during the lunch hour, and as they passed the master's desk they left something for him to sample. Often he refused.

"What's this, coloured all-sorts? Oh no, no. Take them away. Can't stand them. No. It was nice of you to offer, Wilson, but really, you know, they're not very good. You should try the half-penny lollipops. Excellent. First-rate. Or barley sugar; there's something you might like."

There was no obligation upon them to buy sweets and give the master a taster. But woe betide the shameless young miser who bought a nougat, kept it all for himself, and then tried to suck it, without moving his mouth, during afternoon school. Mr. Essand pounced on him and confiscated the entire nougat. Ah, nougat! How Mr. Essand adored it! It clung to his teeth, it sent sweet juices running down his throat, it filled him with wellbeing, contentment, consolation. The life of an elementary schoolmaster could be hard and profitless; some joy there had to be, even for him.

But it was morning still, and Rosenheim was continuing, excitedly:

"The mechanic looked up with a scowl.

41

"How the hell did you get in here?" he said to the three thugs —"

"What was that, Rosenheim?" said Mr. Essand.

"How did you get in here, sir, he said to the three thugs."

"Carry on. My ears must have been deceiving me. I want you boys to pay attention to style. Style is all-important in story-telling."

"So they shoved a spanner in the works, those three tough guys, and they tied the mechanic up with a length of old rope that was lying about, and they left him cursing and swearing —"

"Rosenheim," murmured Mr. Essand with difficulty, since his teeth were caught up in a mass of nougat.

"Bell, sir!" interrupted half-a-dozen voices.

"Ah, playtime —"

There was a mad rush to the door.

"Wait!" thundered Mr. Essand, who could be a disciplinarian when he chose.

"All take your seats!" he shouted angrily. They returned sheepishly to their places.

"Folded arms on desks!" This was the sign of complete obedience.

Mr. Essand's mood had changed, as so often, to one of black ferocity. They sat in absolute silence, while outside in the corridor and above their heads (the Big Boys' playground was on the roof) there was the noise of five hundred railway engines being shattered to fragments with sledgehammers, as the other classes made their way to mid-morning playtime.

"Now," said Mr. Essand, "you may go" — there was a slight, convulsive movement from all forty-five of them — *"one at a time,* beginning with Row One. Binstock, lead off." The rest of the class relapsed into immobility. Already two precious minutes of playtime had been wasted; they dared not risk losing any more, and perhaps having history next lesson into the bargain.

When eight boys had trickled out, Mr. Essand walked

over to the door.

"I'm going to leave you to it," he said. "And I'm going to trust you. And I *warn you,* if any boy goes before his turn, there'll be *trouble!*"

"Has he gone?" they whispered, the very instant he had left the room.

"Yeh, sure!"

"No he hasn't!"

"Yes he has!"

Suddenly, with a sinister glide, Mr. Essand was back in the room. He did not say a word, stood glaring at them for a second, then glided out again.

At last, with a rush, they were up on the roof.

"Hoo-oo!" David shouted and careered around wildly in an overflow of energy. About a hundred other boys were doing the same.

"Hoo-ah! Hoo-ah!" snorted one big fat fellow. "Ah-hoo-ah, ah-hoo-ah, ah-hoo-ah!" He kept up this noise every playtime and all playtime, charging from one corner of the roof to the other.

"Honk-honk! Honk-honk!"

"Git aht ev ahr way! Git aht ev ahr way! Mind yeselves!" shouted a train of boys who swung dangerously in sweeping movements all over the playground, avoiding only the solitary, meditative master who paced slowly, cigarette in hand and eyes on the ground, from the staircase exit to the wall with the stone grille and back again.

The multitudinous criss-crossing of paths and orbits produced collisions and skirmishes, whose shrill hubbub stood out from the steady honk-honking and snorting of school-boy traffic. A hundred feet below, in Dibley Road, a few of the unemployed from the nearby Labour Exchange came daily to watch the infants in their playground and to listen in wonderment to the uproar from above, occasionally craning their necks upwards to see a hand stretched through the stone grille and signalling pointlessly and desperately.

Not everybody was running around chuffing like an

43

engine, hooting like a bus, or knocking over small boys. Against the southern wall, marbles and "glarneys" were being played. It was a serious business to interfere with this sport and its associated commerce. Money was involved.

"I paid fourpence for that lot, you rotter! If you don't help me find every one of them, I'll tell my father. Honest! I mean it! You knocked "em abaht and you can jolly well find "em!"

"A fat lot I care for you *and* your father!"

"Yeh? My father's a bus-driver I can tell you, and he'll knock your father aht any day!"

Son of a bus-driver or not, the victim was usually given right, and the lout who had encroached on to glarney territory was compelled by sheer moral suasion to hunt for the scattered glarneys.

Another area which only a real outsider would violate was the magazine mart which was held beneath the shed in the centre of the playground.

"Last week's *Rover,* a ha'penny!"

"Five old *Magnets,* tuppence!" The *Magnet* and *Gem* did not go down too well in Dibley Road. Only the intellectuals and the snobs preferred them to the thrillers.

"What am I offered for five *Champions* and a *Wizard?*"

"Threeha'pence."

"Gah! Stuff it! They're almost new!"

"I'll give yer last week's *Bull's Eye,* two *Adventures,* and a *Thriller."*

"O.K. Done! There's a pal!"

Most magazines and comics bought and exchanged were for immediate consumer use; but there were speculators even in this market. Fair and keen as it was, it did permit the truly calculating dealer a tiny margin of profit — which, of course, added up after a week's business. Jackie Cohen, for instance, used to make a shilling a week out of the magazine trade. But then, a shilling a week was chicken-feed to Jackie, who was netting four or five shillings a week from glarneys alone. And in the conker season, Jackie went down to Epping Forest and came back, not with a pocketful, or even a bagful, but with a sack....

After play, Mr. Essand was beaming with satisfaction. He had had a nice cup of tea, had emptied his bladder — which was known to give him a lot of trouble — and came back reeking of tobacco. In any case, he was a man of moods, one minute down in the dumps, the next minute chirping with pleasure.

Mr. Essand fetched out the cane, another special feature of his regime. Canes there were in every class, but not like Mr. Essand's. His was scarcely a cane at all, but rather like a toy. They sold canes like it in the oil-shop at the corner — David himself bought one to make a bow-and-arrow with, and it cost only a halfpenny. Whereas the big cane in the hall, which formed part of the Cane and Book, cost sixpence at least. *That* was a cane!

Mr. Essand walked in front of the class, swishing the cane about playfully.

"Now," he asked, "who'd like a swipe? Any volunteers? I'm offering four swipes on the ke-bum-ski, free, gratis, and for nothing. Anybody? Anybody?"

There were no volunteers. The class smiled rather timidly. They were all in the joke, and inured to this harmless pastime; nevertheless, four swipes from Mr. Essand could sting quite a bit, for all that his cane bore no comparison with the real slosher in the hall.

"Come, come," continued Mr. Essand cheerfully, "this won't do at all. What, no volunteers for four swipes? Dear me, you're getting to be a lot of sissies lately!"

They tittered dutifully at the word "sissies", but still no one raised his hand. Mr. Essand went through a sort of ritual song and act. Waving and swishing the cane gently, he intoned:

"I'll give you a swipe!
I'll give you a swipe!
I'll give you a swipe on the ke-bum-ski!
On the ke-bum-ski!
On the ke-bum-ski!"

45

The class laughed a little, very, very quietly and respectfully.

"Well, I'll tell you what I'll do," said Mr. Essand, in tones of mock despair. "I'll make it two. There! I can't do better than that. Two nice little swipes on the ke-bum-ski — any volunteers? Anybody? Anybody?"

Mr. Essand now looked distinctly purposive, and they knew that the real test had come. At any moment, if his desire were thwarted, his facetiousness would change to bitter sarcasm and he would select a compulsory victim on whom to avenge himself.

A few boys put up their hands. They were silly, sloppy youngsters, who thought that by volunteering for a couple of swipes they would find favour with the teacher. Quite the contrary! Mr. Essand was tired of them — always the same lot!

"No, put your hands down," he said. "I don't want *you*. Why shouldn't some of the others take a turn for a change?"

He paused, impatiently slapping his trouser leg with the cane.

"No volunteers? Very well; Rosenheim, come out."

"But *sir!*" Rosenheim gasped at the sheer injustice of it, he, the most popular story-teller in the class, who had this very morning given one of his best instalments from the *Champion*. But that was Mr. Essand's way. He was like some shrewdly capricious potentate, who delighted in upsetting his own puppets, in order to show that apart from himself all men are equal ... less than equal, in fact.

"Rosenheim, come out," he repeated implacably.

Rosenheim clumped over the floorboards to the front of the class, his lips moving in inaudible protest.

"You see, he doesn't like it," said Mr. Essand cheerfully.

At that moment, there was a tap on the door, and the headmaster came into the room. They all bowed their heads in hushed silence over whatever happened to be lying on their desks. Mr. Essand, in no way embarrassed, dismissed Rosenheim in an aside, and cocked his head at

46

the correct angle for a discreet conversation with the headmaster. Their whispered business concluded, the latter then said in a loud voice, "And how are they, Mr. Essand? Are they working well?"

"Most of them," said Mr. Essand. "There are one or two slackers, but we haven't much time for slackers in *this* class."

"Any troublesome ones, send them straight to me. I shall know how to deal with them."

And with a meaningful nod the headmaster walked out of the classroom.

After this delay, Mr. Essand returned briskly to the matter of the swipes. Without further parleying, he gave Rosenheim a couple of swipes on the ke-bum-ski, and to show that there was no ill-feeling, rewarded him with a toffee left over from the previous day's collection. Rosenheim, mollified and reinstated, went back to his desk. He had in any case, like the rest of the class, taken the precaution during playtime of slipping an exercise book into his trouser seat.

2

AVID SHARED a desk with Philip Bernot, a French Jewish boy who lived with his grandfather in Rutherstone Road. Philip's family, the Kleiners, was a large one, intimately associated with David's mother's family, the Levys. His aunts and uncles had appropriate friendships with David's aunts and uncles, just as his mother, Dora Kleiner, was a contemporary and — before her marriage and moving to France — a close friend of David's mother.

Philip took Uncle Yunkel's place to some extent in David's eight-year-old scheme of things. Philip was about a year older than David. He was compact and small — about the same size as Yunkel.

David, having not long returned from Broadstairs Convalescent Home, was rather big and fat, and lumbered around like a tame gorilla by the side of his tiny heroes.

Although David was so much larger, Philip could fight him. This fighting business was very important in Dibley Road School, as elsewhere. It did not mean that much actual fighting took place. What was essential was for each boy to know where he stood and who could fight whom. Usually a boy's position in the fighting hierarchy was established automatically by his size, appearance, origins, and manner. Only when some awkward youngster wanted to break the bounds which nature had imposed upon him was there trouble. Then, a circle was formed in the playground, and threats, snarls of defiance, and wild blows were hurled about amid the howls of the surrounding mob.

Philip and David discussed the matter soberly at the outset of their acquaintance.

"Of course, you're bigger than I am," said Philip, "and you think you can fight me. But you can't, you know."

Unaggressive though David was in these early years, he had to contest this point.

"I could if I was *really wild,*" he said.

"I don't think you could even then," said Philip.

There was nothing for it but a show-down; the uncertainty would otherwise have killed their friendship.

They were strolling along a path on the Dibley Fields, one of the deserted paths which sloped down to the L.N.E.R. railway arches. Peacefully sucking sweets, David suggested a little fight — "not a proper one". Proper fights were very rare and had nothing to do with who could fight whom. The sort of fight David was suggesting was an experimental one, consisting of a long and intense war of nerves, followed by a demonstration show of arms; the whole continuing until one participant became too exhausted to wave his arms any further, or a chance blow was struck, or the threats and fierce gestures really succeeded in arousing the requisite terror.

"Let's finish these bullseyes first," said Philip amicably. It was late afternoon. In the distance, four boys were playing football over a huge pitch, both teams of two chasing and crowding round the soft, listless ball from one goal to the other. An old, bent man with a stick stood on the brow of the slope, turning now towards the four footballers, now towards Philip and David, as they stripped off their overcoats and scarves. They began ... keeping a distance of at least four yards, to begin with. The fireman of an engine that came chuffing slowly down the line from Dibley Junction shouted something derisive. David sailed in, arms flailing round and round like the arms of a windmill.

Philip did more or less the same, though his movements were a little more purposive than David's. There was scarcely a chance of either of them hitting the other except on the top of the head. What troubled David were the tremendously hard knuckles of Philip's fists. Their fists were continually meeting as a result of the energetic circling movements they were making with their arms, and each time their fists met, Philip's iron knuckles stung ferociously. After what was agreed to be "a good fight", David gave in. What was the point of going on, anyway? Someone had to give in, and Philip was obstinate as a mule, so David felt that it was up to him. But good friend that Philip was, he conceded that the issue of what would happen when David was *really wild* should remain undecided. No more than undecided, and probably in Philip's favour even then; but at any rate, undecided.

And as to whether David could wrestle him, that was entirely an open question. Wrestling was different from fighting, and there was no evidence to go on at all. David, for instance, had wrestled and beaten two boys in Class Five; but Philip, they agreed, had only David's word for that. And Philip had wrestled and been beaten by a totally different boy in Class Six; but David had not been present and Philip could have kept the whole thing dark if he had wished. Nor could they put the matter to the test; because for one thing they were both tired, for another, Philip had on his best trousers, and for a third, both of them would cop it for rolling about on the damp grass — and David's mother was a veritable Sherlock Holmes for deducing these things from huge, damp green stains, dust, and caked mud.

So their friendship was fixed, their mutual positions firmly established.

3

WHEN MORNING school was over, Philip and David rushed out to bag a glarney pitch in the alleyway behind the Infants' playground. This was one of the golden moments for marbles, when time had no reality, when past and future fused with the present in eternal bliss. If the sun was shining, so much the better; but if there was a light drizzle, there was no harm done. If there was a steady downpour, that could be tolerated. Only if the rain washed down in sheets and prevented the glarneys from rolling properly was there any serious interference with the game.

When it came to glarneys, David lost his head completely. He caught cold, he wasted all his pocket money, he arrived home an hour late for dinner and had to gollop up his food in order to get back to school on the last stroke of the bell.

But for the first half-hour nothing darkened the pure joy of playing marbles. There they were, all the other dear fellow fanatics, carrying their little bags full of bright, juicy, fat glarneys. And Philip and David laid down their row of three whoppers and shouted with as yet undrained energy and optimism:

"Roll "em up! Roll "em up, me lucky lads! There they are, three lovely ones! Three beauties! All yours, if you can hit "em! Roll "em up! Roll "em up! Three beauties!"

Along came a mournful boy, a born loser, and simply threw away four little ones at their three whoppers; though one of his was found to be cracked.

"Gah! Yer dirty rotter!" David shouted at his retreating, broken back. The mournful boy had not even the heart to reply, but went away to brood for a week over his loss and then to venture another halfpenny on four little ones. Such people! But their triumph was short-lived, because who was this coming along, coolly appraising the merits of each row of glarneys, removing obstructions from the pitch, and rattling a handful of medium-sized, infallible marbles? Yes, it was none other than Jackie Cohen; and behind him, like a vulture, hovered the crooked genius of Jackson, who rolled "em backhandedly.

"'Ullo, Dave," said Jackie. "Let's give you a chance. Can I try a drop shot?"

"Yes," said David, and shut his eyes. Before he had opened them, there was the clash of glass on glass, Jackie had pocketed their three scattered whoppers, and Jackson was waiting for them to put up another three.

Out came another three, and Philip shouted in his piercing voice, "Who's going to 'ave a go 'ere? Three beauties! Three lovely ones! —"

But really there was no need to shout for clients, because Jackson was there, waiting.

"Ready?" said Jackson. "O.K."

Jackson rolled one of his slow, backhanded crawlers. The glarney came wriggling insidiously towards the dead centre of their three; then, by a miracle, hit a bump, turned aside, and missed. His next shot, however, gently tapped the prize, and they were another three down.

Steadily, inevitably, they lost. Philip, moderate and sensible, went home for dinner at one o'clock. David played on with a few little ones he had left. These were suitable only for rolling in the gutter in a game called "spans-ie". "Spans-ie" was decidedly the lowest of marble games. It was slow, and even if a boy lost, nothing definite or irretrievable happened until the last muddy little glarney had rolled within spanning distance of another and the last miserable little bit of credit had been used up. Otherwise the wretched game could go on for ever. Besides, David played it when all his whoppers had been lost, when Philip had wisely deserted home for dinner, and when the very seat of pleasure — the stomach — was barren and full of gloom. Hunger, remorse, despair overwhelmed him. Already, many boys had been home for dinner and returned for afternoon school. If he stayed another five minutes, his mother would come and look for him. While his opponent, even further advanced on the road to self-destruction than David, insisted on finishing the game ...

Pulling himself together at last, he raced home. What joy to find that his mother had a visitor — Maisie, from Shoreditch — and that they had entered into so colossal a conversation, so vast and detailed a review of events since they had last met the previous week, that dinner was only just on the table.

"You see," he said, "it's lucky I didn't come home too early."

4

MORNING SCHOOL in Mr. Essand's class was interesting, and at the same time unpredictable. Anything might happen. There were ups and downs. Mr. Essand might be in a good mood or in a bad mood. Not so in the afternoons. Afternoon school was somnolent, peaceful, and agreeable.

Mr. Essand came back from dinner feeling, like most of the boys, lazy and sleepy. He slumped back in his chair, chin on chest, and stared at the class for five minutes in an effort to make up his mind what to do. On the table in front of him lay the day's quota of lollipops, toffees, liquorice allsorts, sweet gums, bullseyes, peppermints, and chocolate. His clothes, his hands, his breath were permeated with the heavy contentment of tobacco flavoured with beer.

The door was flung open and a couple of latecomers dashed to their desks, gasping and nervous. Mr. Essand said nothing. The cane lay still and forgotten in the drawer. Sluggishly Mr. Essand raised his head and said:

"What would you like, boys?"

"History, sir."

"Jogrefy."

"Sums," said one boy facetiously and was hissed into silence.

"Recitation, sir!" cried a strong pressure group — recitation was their euphemism, and Mr. Essand's, for Bernstein's speedway stories from the *Champion*.

"Chess," insisted a few boys, of whom David was one.

"No, chess later," said Mr. Essand. He was absolutely right, of course; chess never began before three o'clock.

"Well," said Mr. Essand finally, "today *you* are going to do some work for a change —"

"Oh, *sir!*" they groaned in lighthearted protest. Mr. Essand could be trusted to think of nothing that involved effort on his part, and therefore — for they were realists — on their part too.

"Now, now," said Mr. Essand, his eyes almost closed, his breathing heavy. "I want you to learn some poetry. 'To be or not to be, that is the question ...'" He lifted his eyes to the window, as though he were contemplating suicide out of sheer lethargy.

"'To be or not to be, that is the question'" — the words were repeated by the class in a rising clamour.

"Shh!" hissed the monitors from the front corner desk, and looked to Mr. Essand for approval.

"That's right," said the master. "Keep them quiet." He helped himself to some nougat. "Silence!" he barked in a momentary spasm of sternness. "I said, silence! I want you to learn it quietly, to yourselves. When you have learnt it, get on with some reading. Yes, anything," he added impatiently, as some tiresome simpletons put up their hands to ask whether they could read the *Rover*.

In effect, the first hour was given over to the digestion of dinner, the sucking of sweets, and the contemplation through the window of the grey London sky. Millions of people throughout the city were no doubt doing the same thing, looking up from office desks, kitchen sinks, factory benches, and staring through windows covered with grime at the unfathomable sky. It was that sombre, tender hour of the afternoon when eight million digestive systems were gently disposing of twenty-four million potatoes, two or three million cabbages, and a few hundred thousand pounds of meat. Except where, as in Melsham Lane round the corner, the unemployed of those years and the very poor leaned against the walls of the Labour Exchange with nothing to digest.

But while the eyes of their elders were drawn back reluctantly to the figures they were writing, the dishes they were washing, the clothes they were stitching, and the machines they were greasing, the infantile eyes of the boys in Mr. Essand's class were free to roam from the dust on the windows to Mr. Essand's slowly masticating mouth; from the pellets that Shmulevitch and Higgins were catapulting to Mr. Frank Richards' timeless saga in the *Magnet;* from the tense, deadly, silent, and immobile fight going on in desk three of column two, to the bartering of glarneys, conkers, and cigarette pictures taking place in the back desks of columns three and four. In other words, so long as they kept absolutely quiet, Mr. Essand's pupils could do as they liked.

And the poetry which they were supposed to be learning? In this, as in many other matters, there existed a subtle understanding between Mr. Essand and themselves. The poetry was always the same.

"'To be or not to be, that is the question' ..." They were expected to know this passage thoroughly, which was only reasonable. But if they knew it already? If they remembered it from the previous week, and the week before that, and the week before that? Why then, they knew it. No more could be asked of them than that they should know what they were expected to know.

It must not be thought that Mr. Essand was exclusively a lazy man, concerned only with his sweets and his little oddities. David and his fellows did a good deal of work in Mr. Essand's class, though David later found it hard to remember exactly what period of the day was devoted to work, apart perhaps from the first hour or two in the morning. But David did remember that the terms spent with Mr. Essand were far from wasted.

Above all, Mr. Essand showed a noble passion for chess. David did not maintain that chess was necessarily in itself a noble pursuit. But he considered that Mr. Essand's passion for it was noble: when one saw him rise from slothful, post-prandial inertia to get the chess boards; saw the new sense of purpose which animated him, the glitter in his eye, the springiness of his step; saw a man transformed and elevated by the love of abstract truth.

Mr. Essand's conduct of his class was unconventional. Yet to the casual intruder — whether headmaster, fellow-teacher, school monitor, or L.C.C. inspector — the appearance of classroom, teacher, and pupils was unexceptionable. There they were, sitting quietly and peacefully at their tasks. Books lay on the desks, legitimate text-books and exercise books surrounding and hiding the comics and *Champions* and *Adventures*. Was Rosenheim holding forth on the heroes of the speedtrack? Nothing to criticise in that — "recitation", good practice in

55

telling a story. Was Mr. Essand sucking a sweet? Well, why not? Besides, he could swallow it unobtrusively before anyone of importance was able to notice the bulge in his cheek. Was the pile of lollipops and nougats and chocolate a trifle odd? Yes, come to think of it, it was a trifle odd. But then, obviously, all this confectionery had been confiscated from an unusually greedy bunch of little boys who could not wait till school was over before gorging themselves.

When it came to chess, however, the situation was just a little beyond control. Had the games of chess been merely occasional, then the master in charge would have deserved nothing but commendation for showing so progressive and enterprising an educational outlook. But in Mr. Essand's class the enthusiasm both of master and boys passed all reasonable bounds. Every afternoon, from three o'clock onwards, was given over to the analysis of openings, to tourneys, end play, and lightning matches; and not the least excited of the participants was Mr. Essand himself.

So when three o'clock came, Mr. Essand posted a look-out in the corridor.

"Stephenson," he said, "you've been misbehaving." He winked. "You're to stand outside in the corridor for half an hour. Is that quite clear?" He winked again with unmistakable significance.

"Yessir," replied Stephenson, without winking back, for he was their most discreet, as well as their most efficient look-out.

"Now," said Mr. Essand, once Stephenson had gone, "now for some really top-hole play. I want you to do your best this afternoon. We're going to produce a champion in this class, if it's the last thing we do." He rubbed his hands in glee. "Come along! Out with the boards!"

They jumped to it with alacrity. Monitors rushed about with spare pawns and bishops and knights from the class collection. From each desk was produced the sixpenny board and one and threepenny set which they had bought

56

at Mr. Essand's instigation on first entering the class. Someone swiftly cleaned the blackboard so that any interesting situations and problems, as well as the result of their perpetual, recurrent, and overlapping tournaments could be chalked up. During this part of the school day, they gave Mr. Essand their complete loyalty and minute obedience. They were conspirators and experienced the thrill of solidarity.

Play began. Mr. Essand made another attempt to beat Anson, the class prodigy, but within eight moves was hopelessly tied up.

"Will you keep *quiet!*" he exclaimed irritably to the class in which there was not a murmur.

Stephenson suddenly poked his head into the room. A frenzied movement began to clear away all the boards and pieces, when Stephenson called in a low voice:

"O.K.! False alarm!"

Mr. Essand's head remained bowed over his game, unaware of the momentary panic which had seized the class. They found it such a responsibility to look after him. Once chess had begun, he entered a sort of trance. He was still in a daze, when, the alarm having been given, they urged him, almost pushed him to his rightful position in front of the class. There was a flurry of movement, a mass of books, papers, pens appeared on their desks; Mr. Essand took a piece of chalk and wrote uncertainly on the board:

PB8

They gaped — had he gone off his head? Poor, dear Mr. Essand, they felt like saying, pull yourself together, quickly, quickly! — Too late...

The headmaster entered the room, whispered something in Mr. Essand's ear about the timetable, then said in the rich, loud voice reserved for the boys' benefit:

"I see that boy Stephenson has been misbehaving again. I warn you all," he said, turning to the class, "that I am giving my attention — *personally* — to any boy who persistently misbehaves. Do you know what I caught him doing, Mr. Essand? I caught him peeping into this classroom even after he'd been sent out into the corridor. He denied it, of course. But I saw him doing it myself from the hall."

The headmaster looked at the board. "How are they getting on, Mr. Essand? There are some bright boys in this class, as well as some bad ones." He looked at the board again, distinctly puzzled. Nothing on it but a huge:

PB8

The eyes of the class, too, were hypnotised by those symbols. Finally Mr. Essand followed the general gaze. They all stared at the offending announcement:

PB8

Mr. Essand, brought to his senses, was equal to the situation.

"Aha," he said with jovial confidence. "They have been very good today — apart, I must say, from Stephenson. I promised them a little chemistry — nothing practical, of course, just theory."

The headmaster still looked somewhat dubiously at the blackboard.

"They are beginning to understand," said Mr. Essand, "the importance of chemical formulae. Thus, PB is the formula for lead, 8 gives the number of molecules. PB 8 is chemical shorthand for eight molecules of lead ..."

The headmaster withdrew quietly from the room, so as not to interrupt Mr. Essand's dissertation. The old man — he was white-haired and very old, one of the first generation produced by the 1870 Education Act — felt gratified to discover that the more far-seeing members of his staff were pushing ahead with the scientific side of the syllabus. One must march with the times.

When the headmaster had gone, Anson said laconically:

"PB 8 would be no good, sir."

"And why not, may I ask?" said Mr. Essand with heat.

"Because I should check with my knight, exchange knight for bishop, and get your pawn by discovered check."

Mr. Essand's jaw hung down. "Uh? ..." he said. "Uh? But ... Hm." He rubbed the bristles on his chin.

But it was true. They could all see it — PB 8 would lose him the game.

5

D AVID AND Philip began their games of chess in school and finished them at home, or they began them at home and finished them at school. They never separated without having begun a game to think over before their next meeting. Nor did they need to note down the position of the pieces. The layout of the board they had just left was as firmly fixed in their brains as the geography of the streets of Hackney.

Chess, for some reason, met with the approval of their families. The grown-ups did not play themselves, except for old Mr. Kleiner, David's grandfather, who shifted the pieces cannily and disconcertingly and annoyed David and Philip by ignoring the advice of the text-books and winning nonetheless. But they gathered round and made admiring comments.

"You need brains to play this game. It'd be no use me trying."

"I started to learn once, but I gave it up. There's so many different moves. Not like draughts."

"If only they'd always sit quietly like this, instead of running around the streets. I saw David shouting himself hoarse the other evening over his blessed glarneys, just like some rough goy."

"Philip's just as bad, only he doesn't show it so much."

"I don't know which is the bigger lobbus of the two."

"Philip's older, he ought to have more sense."

"They'll grow out of it."

"Do you think so? Sometimes I wonder."

"Anyway, as long as they're playing, it's already good."

"You wonder people don't get tired of it, the same old thing again and again."

Meanwhile, impervious to such frivolities, the boys' minds soared through the pure logic of permutation and combination.

The chessboard certainly gave the final touch to a cheerful domestic scene. On Saturday evenings in winter, for instance, the fire was piled high and chestnuts were roasted. Sofa and chairs were drawn up round the deep red coals, and at the apex of this triangle, David and Philip sat over their game. They did not look up as the hot chestnuts and cups of tea were handed to them, though from time to time their hands reached out blindly over the table to feel for some of the tasty remnants of tea and beginnings of supper. Behind each of them stood always a couple of uncomprehending, observant, and deeply interested spectators. If they were in Philip's house, the spectators might be Philip's Auntie Esther, Auntie Deborah and Auntie Netta, or Uncle Hymie and Uncle Abie, or Bertie Mackson, who lived with the Kleiners; or they might be Uncle Sid and Auntie Fay, who, though they lived on the first floor of David's Uncle Harry's house, of which the Hirsches occupied the basement, might well be visiting Philip's grandparents, that is to say Auntie Fay's parents. In David's house there was an even greater number of potential spectators — Auntie Debby, Auntie Rachel, Auntie Esther, Auntie Rosie, Auntie Bessie, Uncle Isaac, Uncle Harry, Auntie Sadie, Uncle Pinchas, Uncle Jake, and even Uncle Yunkel, who said emphatically that he did not understand "a blind word of chess, because the Talmud was far more deep."

After having begun a game to cogitate overnight, David and Philip left, amid great opposition, to roam the streets. It was Saturday night, and there was much to see, much territory to explore. They might go first to the flea-pit in Shoreditch and see Tom Mix in a cowboy film for tuppence; or, in greater style, to the Clarence, in Lower Clapton, there to yell and whistle and stamp in their thrupenny seats every time the Buster Keaton film broke down. But on the whole, they preferred to keep in the open and "explore".

Exploration with Uncle Yunkel had been vast and sketchy. David and Yunkel flung out their outposts to Hampstead and Purley and Wandsworth and Richmond, but failed to hold these enormous tracts of territory. They might carve their initials on a tree in Clapham Common, but on returning four months later, they scarcely even knew the right tram-stop at which to get off. On the other hand, exploration with Philip, if less ambitious, was more thorough. David and Philip set out to conquer only the boroughs immediately bordering Hackney, Dalston and Dibley — Stamford Hill, Stoke Newington, Clapton, Homerton, Cambridge Heath, and Bethnal Green on the one side; and Highbury, Islington, Hoxton, and Shoreditch on the other.

It was necessary to know every alley, every cul-de-sac, every arch, every passageway; every school, every hospital, every church, every synagogue; every police station, every post office, every labour exchange, every lavatory; every curious shop name, every kids' gang, every hiding-place, every muttering old man or woman whose appearance alone was enough to terrify them. In fact everything; and having got to know everything, they had to hold this information firmly, to keep abreast of change, to locate the new position of beggars, newsboys, hawkers, street shows, gypsies, political meetings.

"You can't beat Saturday night," said Philip.

"You bet your life," David replied. "Where shall we go? Down Ridley?"

There was much for them to do in Ridley Road market. They had to check up on King Anthony, heir, so he claimed, to the throne of England, descendant of the Tudors and street-corner politician. He had not been seen for several weeks; was he back on his pitch? Then there was the man who swallowed fire — did he *really* swallow fire? They had to edge up close, almost under his very mouth, to solve *that* mystery, while at the same time ready to squeeze back through the crowd and disappear the moment his mate came round with the collecting box. The man who had himself manacled and fettered and then broke a steel chain — something else to keep an eye on, though it was obviously phoney, the whole business. Then there were the stalls. They had to make an up-to-the-minute survey of the novelty market, the yo-yos, stinkbombs, children's cigarettes, sixpenny cameras and torches.

As for torches, those in themselves might occupy them the whole evening if they were not careful. On their patrols of North-East London they needed the most powerful torches possible. They might be trapped in a dark street and want to signal into the sky. They might have to illuminate a dangerous alley beset with kidnappers — they had read about those enemies of childrenkind in the newspapers, and even their parents had warned them to run away from suspicious strangers. They might need to blind with torch dazzle the eyes of an attacking gang in Shoreditch or Hoxton. Power was what they were looking for, sheer incandescent kilowatt power. And there was no end to their search for bigger and brighter bulbs, cheaper and yet more powerful batteries, which could indefinitely be rebaked to potency.

So Ridley it was. Yes, King Anthony was back, surrounded by a large crowd which listened seriously and even glumly to his analysis of Tudor and Hanoverian genealogy. The fire-swallowing man was there, furiously swallowing fire — "ah, to hell with the man!" they decided. "Let him go on swallowing fire!" The manacled man writhed among his chains. There was a sharp snap which they thought at first might be his red and bursting neck, but which turned out to be the thick, massive steel chain again... Everything was in order. Philip found an enormous torch bulb going for tuppence, which they bought between them on their complicated, bickering system of mutual credit and use. The fishmongers, clothes dealers, cut-price confectioners, whelk-sellers, oyster-mongers, tattooists, blowers up of balloons, clair-voyants, comic-dealers, and discreet salesmen of toilet goods, murmured their comments, roared their cries, muttered their curses; while bulging housewives, and others with pinched faces and five or six pale, snotty, whimpering children, protested and fingered and shoved. Amid the hoarse cries, the heaving crowd, and beneath the flickering, lurid light of flares hissing from the tops of stalls, David and Philip wormed their way, holding hands for safety.

Suddenly, David didn't know how, Philip's hand was no longer there. David turned this way and that. He pushed and squirmed and shouted. He asked a huge stallkeeper with bright, cheerful boils on his neck whether he could see David's friend. But in vain; Philip was lost. Then David remembered their secret call, to be used only in dire emergency. He cupped his hands to his mouth and uttered a piercing, shrieking yodel:

"Yowee! Yowee! Yowee! Yoweeyoweeyoweeyowee-yowee!" There was no reply. He tried again, louder and shriller than ever:

"Yoweeyoweeyowee! Yoweeyoweeyowee! Yowee! Yowee!"

Faintly, through the turmoil, came the sound of its twin, Philip's answering call:

"Yoowiyoowi! Yoowiyoowi! Yoowiyoowiyoowiyoowi!" Like ships signalling in the night, their craft guided themselves through the tumultuous human waves. All was well.

6

WHEN DAVID was almost ten and Philip almost eleven, their combination was broken up. To the utter confusion of their joint finances, of their finely split and interpenetrated ownership of glarneys, conkers, cigarette pictures, stamps, comics, and chessmen, and to the ruination of their development in chess, Philip's father came over from Paris and took Philip back with him to France. So arbitrarily did parents and adults generally intrude on infantile existence. Philip never returned to England.

But they met again, David and Philip. Two months before the war, one hot Sunday afternoon in July, 1939, David took the metro to Aubervilliers, on the outskirts of Paris. It was a quarter of Paris rarely visited by the English visitor unless he were attracted by the market, which reminded David of their own Ridley Road Market in Dalston. In Aubervilliers, however, there was poverty — colourful, indeed, but annihilating — of a kind unknown in England. David made his tweed-jacketed way among the same pale-faced women with their trains of five or six whimpering children. Gruff, stubble-chinned workmen, in cap and blouse, sat on the terraces of bare-boarded cafés with rickety, trestle tables.

David walked up the hot, dusty Avenue Marton, lined with shanties, tenements, and industrial buildings, till he found the courtyard he was looking for. He was at once surrounded by a little crowd of urchins.

"Can you tell me where Mr. Bernot lives?" he asked in French.

Though his French, David felt confident, was excellent, the children did not reply, but stared at him in amazement. Finally, to his relief, a young man wearing a workman's cap ambled up.

"Can you please tell me where Mr. Bernot lives?" David asked the young man, while the youngsters formed an open-mouthed circle around them.

"Which Mr. Bernot do you wish to see?" the young man asked rather wearily.

Then something familiar about the young man's features and voice electrified David.

"Why, Mr. Philip Bernot, of course!" he replied, and grasped the other's hand. "Philip!"

"You are someone from England," said the young man, "but who? Can it be David?"

Stooping to get through the low door, David was led into the elder Mr. Bernot's little workshop, where Philip and his brothers too were employed. David and Philip went through to the back, into a bare-boarded living-room, and sat down at a clothless table covered with cigarette ash and spilt coffee. Philip said bitterly:

"You see how we live here…. It's work that does it, work and poverty. They brutalise us."

During the German occupation of France, most of Philip's family suffered the fate of five million Jews and were starved and done to death in an extermination camp. Philip himself went underground and escaped. After the war he returned to live once again in Paris, in Aubervilliers.

PART THREE
THE RACHAM

1

NOT ALL synagogues were alike. The United Synagogue, with its established funds and well-defined hierarchy, could be compared to the official church. The Federation of Synagogues could be compared to the major dissident churches. As for the Chassidic synagogues, they were unique. In their independence, their occasional oddities of belief, and their tendency towards fragmentation, they bore some resemblance to the chapels and prayer-houses of revivalist sects. But their gaiety, their unpredictability, their rapid foundation, disappearance, and reappearance, their pickled-herring snacks, their extraordinary timetable, their roystering choruses, their violent quarrels and long-matured feuds, their genuine religious fervour combined with cheerfulness, lack of ceremony, and, one might almost say, bohemianism — with what could these be compared?

The United Synagogue was the most anglicised of the synagogues. If they were scheduled to begin service at nine o'clock, they began at nine o'clock, or even — to show themselves more English than the English — at ten to nine. If the service in a Federation synagogue was due to start at nine, the beadle and wardens became restless as the clock struck the hour, but they did nothing until, say, three minutes past nine. Traditionalists, as well as Englishmen, they made this small demonstration of respect to immemorial Jewish conceptions of time. The Chassidim, of course, just did as they pleased. They were usually not scheduled to

66

begin at any special time, and if there was some vague, half-humorous suggestion such as — "At any rate, no later than ten!" or, "Anyway, so's we can finish, without rushing, by twelef o'clock!" — the chance of this hour being adhered to was no greater and no less than that of any other hour in the day's twenty-four.

David's father was a member of the Federation of Synagogues, but the times of the services at the Chassidic synagogues suited him better. So Mr. Hirsch and David gradually tended to go on Friday evenings, and later on Saturday mornings, not to the Federation Synagogue, where David's grandfather was beadle, but to the Racham Chassidic Synagogue, also known as Brodkof's. It was two rooms made into one by the pulling down of the intervening wall, and it was situated on a ground floor in Rutherstone Road. Most people knew it as Brodkof's, because Mr. Brodkof settled the rent, supplied the coal in winter, and paid the electricity bill — often late, as the congregation knew when the electricity was cut off and services had to be held by the light of two candles. The installation of a slot-meter for electricity did not dispose of this last difficulty, because the number of pennies necessary for a Friday evening service was often too finely calculated; no money could be handled on the Sabbath, which began at nightfall on Friday, the lights snapped off in the middle of the service, and they were back where they started.

However, the Racham was Brodkof's synagogue. But Brodkof was not the most important man in the Racham. Far from it. Mr. Firmann, Mr. Kembell, Mr. Stannenberg, Mr. Cohen from Rutherstone Road, and Mr. Cohen from Dibley Road were all at *least* as important as Mr. Brodkof. The Chassidim were individualists; if Brodkof wanted to act like he owned the whole world just because he paid the rent, then he had come to the wrong place!

It was just possible that a man of immense verve, a rapid, vehement talker, a banger of tables, a furious, self-assertive vower by the Holy Scroll of the Law and upon

67

his own dear mother's life, and who in addition paid the rent and the electricity bill, supplied the candles and the pickled herring, it was just possible that he might have dominated the Chassidim. But what did Brodkof do? He went white in the face, he bit his thin, lower lip, he paced up and down at the back of the Racham, and he *cried*. Yes, David himself saw Brodkof cry on several occasions. David saw a couple of small tears trickle down Brodkof's cheeks and heard something between a cough and a sob break from his throat.

It was all over nothing at all, the tiniest of tiny trifles.

"Let's start," said Brodkof on Friday evening, when it was quite dark outside and the other synagogues had long finished their service. No one took any notice of him. Everybody went on talking loudly and animatedly.

"Let's start," repeated Brodkof. He was foolish, of course. He should have got round Firmann and Stannenberg quietly beforehand. Then, if all three had together banged the large, sloping-topped chest which stood in the front of the synagogue near the Ark, and if they had simultaneously shouted, "Let's start!", there would have been a chance of the Racham taking notice. As it was, Brodkof said for the third time, "Let's start," and no one bothered with him.

He tried shouting, though his voice at its loudest was little more than an ineffectual piping:

"Let's start, I say, let's start!"

Thin though his shout had been, it accomplished one thing, never very difficult to accomplish; it aroused Firmann's choking rage.

"And I say no!" choked Firmann.

"And I say yes!"

"And I say no!"

"And I say yes!"

Others joined in to support Firmann.

"And I say no! And I say no! And I say no!"

"Yes, yes!"

"No, no!"

68

"Yes!"

"No!"

Then it was that Brodkof retired to the back of the synagogue, white with fury, and paced up and down biting his thin lower lip and crying. But Firmann had a good heart; so had Stannenberg, so had Kembell. As soon as they saw Brodkof's piteous condition, they trailed after him. Also pacing up and down, they turned when he turned, they stopped when he stopped.

"Listen, Brodkof," said Firmann. "Don't take it like that..."

"Brodkof, you mustn't take it like that," said Stannenberg.

"It's just that we didn't think everyone had arrived yet," said Kembell.

"Every other synagogue," muttered Brodkof, "every other synagogue has finished long ago — not started, but finished! And we haven't even started...."

"All right," said Firmann, "so let's start. Gentlemen!" he shouted, "let's start! It's late enough already, so let's start!"

"Let's start!" echoed Stannenberg.

"Come on everybody!" called Kembell, "it's time to start!"

Firmann put his arm round Brodkof, and wheedled him back to the front of the synagogue. The congregation all felt glad that the row was over. Brodkof's pale, miserable face brightened up a little, he smiled feebly. Firmann smiled and chuckled. Kembell gave a croaking laugh. Stannenberg sang a quaint tarradiddle. Everyone smiled and laughed and they all urged each other to their seats. They all loudly told each other to stop talking and banged the backs of the benches to secure silence. There was a great din as everybody shouted — "Silence! Silence! Enough already! Let's start!"

The arguments were not quite over, because Brodkof had still to be persuaded to sing the evening service as cantor.

"Come on, Brodkof," said Stannenberg.

"No, you, Stannenberg!"

"No, come on Brodkof, give us a good tune."

"Stannenberg, do me a favour —"

"Ach! Brodkof, leave me alone, don't make no business —"

"Come on, Stannenberg." Brodkof pushed Stannenberg gently towards the cantor's stand. Stannenberg at the same time pushed Brodkof. Firmann was involved somehow, either pushing them both or separating them, Kembell stood nearby and expostulated generally. Suddenly Brodkof gave way. Without the slightest further argument, he walked swiftly over to the cantor's stand, dextrously manoeuvred the prayer-shawl over his head in a couple of movements, and began to intone. He intoned for about five minutes on the same vowel, going upwards and downwards, backwards and forwards, in and out, round and round, over and under, betwixt and between, then up and down again, and over and under ... The congregation waited. Finally, when Brodkof's voice had finished chanting that one unfortunate vowel, he tore through the remainder of the service at a speed which gratified those at the back, "the boys", but scandalised the religious elders at the front. At such a speed, they declared, the service was invalid.

"Insane," said the others, "there's no getting away from it, he's insane."

Brodkof was now a transformed man. He hummed cheerfully to himself, he folded the prayer-shawl, he ignored all the remarks which were passed about him, was not in the least bit touchy.

"Gentlemen," he said, "now we can go home to the wives, who are waiting with supper, the good old supper, with fried fish and wine. I ask you, what is there to beat a Jewish Friday night?"

"Insane," still grumbled some of the elders. "A madness has taken hold of the world."

2

THERE WAS once an American song with the chorus: "I like sociability, for sociability's sake, for sociability's sake!"

That was how Brodkof felt about the Racham; it explained why he ran the Racham. The Chassidim never asked themselves why Brodkof settled the rent, paid for the coal, and so on; they took sociability for granted, whereas Brodkof was continuously, actively, and consciously engaged in promoting sociability. On Friday evenings, Saturday mornings, and Saturday evenings, before, during, and after services, there was at the Racham all the sociability a man could desire. Too much sociability, even; it interfered with the service and ignored the organisation which Brodkof had put in during the week. The correspondence which the synagogue received, the final notices of bills long overdue with the penalties for non-payment heavily underlined in red type, were left on the table for all to see. Occasionally Brodkof drew Firmann and Stannenberg and Kembell aside, and in a loud private argument pointed out the crippling cost of running the synagogue. He did so, less in the hope of persuading them to contribute towards the bills, than in order somehow to get the Chassidim to recognise, to be aware of, to have some faint inkling of all that he was doing for sociability's sake. But the correspondence was scattered about the synagogue or used to light cigarettes from the fire immediately the Sabbath was over and smoking once again permitted. Firmann and Stannenberg and Kembell completely missed the main issue by abusing the Gas Company, the Electricity Company, the landlords, and the coalman for sending in such outrageous bills. As for the threats heavily underlined in red type, they told Brodkof not to worry. So long as he paid eventually, it did not matter how late he was; his credit was good, everybody knew that. If he had been a pauper, it would have been different.

The fact was that Brodkof did not receive proper recognition because of the very success of his efforts for sociability's sake. There was so much sociability in the Racham on Friday evening, Saturday morning, and Saturday evening, that no one thought of what they owed to Brodkof. The curious thing was, that in spite of this lack of recognition, Brodkof wanted still more sociability. There was Saturday afternoon, for instance, the long Saturday afternoons in summer, from three o'clock till seven. The Racham was quite empty then. Why shouldn't there be a men's club to hold meetings and discussions over tea and biscuits? He, Brodkof, would willingly supply the first fortnight's biscuits, and after the first fortnight they could see .... perhaps a small contribution from each member... The Chassidim discussed with animation the possibility of holding discussions, but they were not willing to hold the actual discussions. For one thing, Saturday afternoon was a time set aside for sleeping; for another, they just somehow didn't fancy it....

That was how the matter stood for several years. Then a new generation arose, "the boys at the back": Sammy, Theodore, Elijah, and David. Brodkof's eyes lit up as he watched their developing sociability. He chided them gently, without any real recrimination, when they talked during the service. He patted them on the back, pointed them out with pride to visitors. "The boys", he said, the new generation.

When the time was ripe, and they were about eleven years old, he called them together at the back of the synagogue, pinched their cheeks, and explained: "Here you are," he said, "four of you, four boys. Nice boys, of good families —"

Elijah Stannenberg chortled.

"No, I mean it," continued Brodkof, and shook his head up and down in vigorous affirmation. "Really nice boys of really good families. Clever boys. Good boys. Boys who like a game, a laugh. And sports also. And going out sometimes, seeing places, seeing what sort of a world this is we live in. Everything. Why don't you form a club?" he asked quietly. His face was grave, even sad, as he put the question; his eyes were momentarily downcast. "Yes," he said, "why don't you form a club?" He stretched his hand out forwards and downwards as far as it would go, in a gesture emphasising the simplicity and inevitability of his proposition; the solution, his raised eyebrows and small, wide-open eyes seemed to say, the solution to the whole problem, to everything in fact.

"Yes," said Theodore, "why not?" He shrugged his shoulders and diplomatically puckered his face in the manner of their elders.

"It's not a bad idea," said Sammy, also intuitively diplomatic.

"I think it's a jolly good idea," said David.

"And I think it's a lousy idea!" said Elijah in his rather screechy voice.

"Now, now, Elijah," said Stannenberg, who had been hovering on the edge of the group to keep an eye on his son. "You mustn't use expressions like that. They're not nice, they're nasty. Feh! Lousy! ... A louse is a minute animal which crawls on the heads of dirty people —"

"I don't care if it's a minute banimal!" said Elijah. "I don't care if it's a minute shanimal! I don't care if it's a minute cannibal! It's an expression which conveys a certain meaning to the listener, and I'm entitled to use it if it suits my purpose."

Stannenberg led Elijah off, expostulating in lengthy phrases, trying at the same time to soothe, to instruct, to remonstrate, and to edify.

These odd and for the most part good-tempered scenes were always occurring between Stannenberg and Elijah. Elijah did not really want to come to the synagogue at all. He was so reluctant to do so that he used to stand in the passage in sheer distaste, until his father saw him and hurried over with a prayer-shawl.

"Ah! There you are, Elijah. You've somewhat procrasti-

73

nated in coming to worship, haven't you? And why do you stand in the passage? You should have proceeded without delay to your seat."

Then the others would hear a muttered argument from which Stannenberg's voice rose. "Oh, fiddlesticks, Elijah! Fiddlesticks!"

Elijah's voice eventually rose, too, before his final capitulation. "Your argument is based on entirely false premises," they could hear. Elijah's voice insisted monotonously, in the weary tone of one who must humour an obstinate child. "I've told you before that Darwin's theory of evolution proves that religion is nothing but a collection of primitive superstitions. Go to the Natural History Museum —"

"Elijah! Elijah! Such blasphemous talk is foolish nonsense. You're being childish."

"Science has proved —"

"Ach! Hush! A scandal! What is this, a synagogue or a public-house!" cried the elders from within the synagogue. "Insanity! A madness has taken hold of the world."

"You see, Elijah," murmured Stannenberg. "You see what you've done." Elijah, having registered his protest, and with an expression of invincible disgust, then took his place along with "the boys" on the dusty backbenches.

So it was on this occasion. They heard Elijah protesting and caught such phrases as "the law of the conservation of energy", "Einstein's theory of relativity", and then Elijah rejoined them.

"All right," he said wearily, "let's form a club."

The club was formed to meet on Saturday afternoons. Brodkof supplied lemonade, biscuits, sweets, fruit, and chocolate. Brodkof found another boy named Goldberg to share them with David and his friends. But somehow, knowing that they were supposed to enjoy themselves, that they had got to enjoy themselves, they found it difficult to occupy the time. David suggested debates, but these usually got no further than: "Mr. Chairman, I beg to propose that this House —"

"Mr. Chairman, on a point of order —"

"Mr. Chairman!"

"Mr. Chairman!"

"Mr. Chairman, I beg to —"

"Mr. Chairman!"

"Order! Order!"

Then, after rolling with laughter for a couple of minutes, they still had nothing to do. The lemonade was drunk, the biscuits were all eaten up. It only remained for Mr. Brodkof to poke his head benignly round the door.

"Enjoying yourselves, boys?"

"Yes, Mr. Brodkof. Very nice. Very nice."

"Good, good. Enjoy yourselves, that's the way."

The club lasted a couple of months. Then the opportunity occurred to wind it up without offending Brodkof. It was superseded by something altogether bigger, something which spread beyond the bounds of mere sociability. Instead of occupying the Racham only on Saturday afternoons, a plan was drawn up and put into effect whereby the boys should occupy it every evening. At Brodkof's instigation, their parents had decided, not without grave doubts and misgivings, to found a talmudical and theological college in the Racham itself, and they were to be the students.

3

RABBI SBORODINOVICH had just arrived from Poland. Time was, when the ships used to dock by Tower Bridge, and the immigrants into England could disappear without further ado among the streets and courts of the East End, there to begin life afresh. But all that had changed. Now, a permit was required from the Home Office. And to obtain a permit it was necessary for the applicant to show that employment was awaiting him which could not be undertaken by a British subject. So it was arranged that Rabbi Sborodinovich should become officiating rabbi of the Racham. Clearly, this was a post which could not easily be filled by any British subject. Two men from the Home Office came down and looked over the Racham; their permission was given and Rabbi Sborodinovich was allowed to enter the country.

There was not, in the first place, much that Rabbi Sborodinovich could do at the Racham. They were not accustomed to a rabbi. They were a free-and-easy synagogue and his presence produced a certain constraint. Once he was urged to deliver a sermon. He pointed out, very politely and obliquely, their moral shortcomings. They looked at each other awkwardly, they crossed and uncrossed their legs uneasily. To whom was he referring in his remarks about "this present generation", "laxity", "epicureanism", and "those who made a joke of everything, unaware of the terrible punishment which was to come"? He could hardly mean Brodkof, or even Firmann, Stannenberg, and Kembell. Actually he was staring out into the distance towards the back of the room, where "the boys" were sitting. One or two of the elders glanced in that direction. *They* knew to whom he was referring — those who talked during service! Gradually the atmosphere became easier, the realisation dawned on all the adults present that Rabbi Sborodinovitch must undoubtedly be addressing himself to "the boys", the boys at the back. After all, rabbi though he might be, he could hardly have the nerve to say such things about *them,* when they had got him into the country ... and everything.

He was not again asked to deliver a sermon. One was enough; the lesson had been brought home. Talking during service must stop. After the sermon, the elders frowned at the boys, they clucked reprovingly. "A scandal," they muttered. "Insanity. A madness has come on the world."

Meanwhile the parents of David and his friends were concerting practical measures. Brodkof was with them, too, full of ambitious schemes for the future of the Racham. Why, it was asked, should the boys have to dash off every evening to the East End for their talmudical instruction, when they had with them on their very doorstep so learned and devout a rabbi as Rabbi Sborodinovich? Why, indeed, except that their parents were conservative and did not like chopping and changing in these matters. But, argued Brodkof, there need be no chopping and changing; one chop and change would be sufficient. After that, as far ahead as anyone could see, the boys would be students of the Racham Talmudical College, which could do for Hackney what the Yeshivah Talmudical College had done for the East End.

The Saturday afternoon club was quietly dropped. Instead, Sammy, Theodore, Elijah, Goldberg, and David, as well as five newly recruited and totally unrelated boys named Cohen, went to the Racham on Sunday mornings and every weekday evening in order "to learn".

In the Yeshivah Talmudical College, David had been learning the chapter which begins: "Two men seize a prayer-shawl. This one says, *I* found it, and this one says, *I* found it...." As a matter of fact, David had not been doing too well at that chapter. He came late to classes, he daydreamed, he made excuses for getting off early. His relatives said that it was probably because the rabbi at the Yeshivah Talmudical College had not made "Two men seize a prayer-shawl" interesting enough. It was the duty of a teacher to make the Talmud interesting, to hold the attention even of a somewhat frivolously minded boy like David. Perhaps, also, "Two men seize a prayer-shawl" was not the right chapter for a boy of eleven. Therefore the switchover to Rabbi Sborodinovich might be just the change that was necessary, apart from saving David the daily journey to the East End.

With Rabbi Sborodinovich the boys learnt the chapter which begins, "An ox gores a cow, whether on the public highway or on private property — who is liable?" Here, said David's relatives, is the chance to show what you can do, with a new chapter, an absorbing and exciting chapter, and a first-rate teacher who knows how to make the Talmud interesting. David himself thought that he might do better on "An ox gores a cow". But it did not take him long to experience the same sense of defeat and gloom at the sight of "An ox gores a cow" as had afflicted him in the East End at the sight of "Two men seize a prayer-shawl". The fault, he began to feel — and subsequent years confirmed his childish intuition — did not lie with Rabbi Sborodinovich, nor with the rabbi at the Yeshivah Talmudical College, nor with "Two men seize a prayer shawl", nor with "An ox gores a cow", nor even with himself. The cause was more fundamental and quite inescapable; he was "allergic" to the Talmud. There existed between himself and the Talmud an irreconcilable incompatibility.

At the age of eleven, however, he could only sense these things. He could not express himself, except by coming late, daydreaming, making excuses for going home early, and buying stinkbombs and explosive caps.

4

RABBI Sborodinovich's class at the Racham very soon split up into the majority which did not buy stinkbombs and explosive caps, and the minority which did. The minority consisted of Elijah, one of the five distinct Cohens, and David. They did not really know what they were doing in buying those dreadful things. They were, after all, only children. It was so easy to walk into the sweet-shop, plank down a penny, and leave with a harmless-looking glass phial of a stinkbomb; or to plank down another penny and walk out with four harmless-looking, tiny, screwed-up balls of paper containing a few grains of explosive. If any blame was to be apportioned, the authorities who permitted the sale of those noxious baubles, and the shop-keeper who for mere gain sold them, *they* should have received the major share. The boys, for their part, did no more than throw them into corners of the Racham, a simple act, surely, in itself of little consequence.

Yet the effects of this simple act were terrible, for it released upon the Racham all the dark forces which the fiendish ingenuity of the manufacturers, with their research chemists, their powerful machines, and their up-to-date industrial organisation, could concentrate into a tiny bauble sold for a penny over the shop counter.

The stinkbombs were probably more vicious than the explosive caps; and in addition they were silent, their action was delayed, their effect was long and heart-breakingly difficult to counteract, and the culprit responsible for them was almost impossible to detect. Truly those stinkbombs were evil. Their smell was monstrously disgusting, they opened to the mind undreamt of and otherwise unimaginable hells. One alone, in the furthest corner of the room was sufficient to render Rabbi Sborodinovich's position untenable. The room had to be evacuated and the lesson abandoned for at least half an hour. Indeed, the stinkbombs were so abominable that one of the Cohens and David took fright. They could not go through with the campaign. They became sick at heart when the first nauseating whiff drifted over from a broken phial. Though all the boys laughed in the passage outside — even Rabbi Sborodinovich smiled wanly at the first few stinkbombs — there was fear and disquiet in their laughter. Such foulness as that which had just been perpetrated in the Racham could not go unpunished; it was wicked, truly evil.

One of the Cohens and David, as has been said, very soon backed out of the stinkbomb campaign. Rabbi Sborodinovich looked forlorn. Those bombs really had knocked the fight out of him. Only Elijah was inhumanly content.

"H_2S, that's all it is," he said. "Maybe there are one or two refinements as well. I wonder who did it; sure it wasn't you, Theodore?"

Theodore grinned, because they all knew that he positively enjoyed the Talmud, as he enjoyed every difficult mental activity, thus coming top in every subject in every class he had ever been in at school.

"Are you sure it wasn't you?" replied Theodore.

Rabbi Sborodinovich looked at Elijah with the ultimate hatred of a mild man provoked beyond endurance. He waited, however, to catch Elijah in the act, because otherwise Mr. Stannenberg would have been offended. "My Elijah!" he would have said. "A playful youngster, I know; but commit an outrage like that! Never! ..."

But the situation resolved itself. Suddenly Elijah had had enough, not merely of the stinkbombs, but of the Talmud, the Racham, and everything connected with Jewish tradition, learning, and religion. He refused to come even as far as the passage for Friday and Saturday services, and of course he stayed away from evening classes.

After the departure of Elijah and the stinkbombs, there still remained the explosive caps. They were, so to speak, clean weapons. There was no smoke; they exploded with a sharp, loud bang, made the whole class jump simultaneously in their chairs, and that was that. It was easy to throw them with a quick, imperceptible flick of the wrist. The explosion came from the faraway corner where they struck the wall or the floor. Who was responsible now that Elijah had left? Rabbi Sborodinovich made some ballistic calculations whereby suspicion fell on one of the Cohens and David. One day he actually saw David throwing the infuriating cap. He lost his temper. "Wild beast!"

he shouted at David. "Hound! All black years you bring upon me!" He came at David with fist upraised. David dodged round the first row of seats on which the congregation sat at week-ends. Rabbi Sborodinovich followed. David dived into the fourth row. Rabbi Sborodinovich turned back to block the exit. David climbed over two rows of seats into the sixth row, crashed along it, and bolted into the passage and out into the street.

David was sent back to the Yeshivah Talmudical College, where they were used to handling the toughest boys in the East End and the rabbis knew how to lay about them. There David reverted to his more usual role of meek and mild recalcitrant, a daydreamer, a late-comer, a maker of excuses for getting off early.

With all the excitement over, the other students at the Racham very soon began to drop off. They found it frankly dull, sitting there evening after evening, just the handful of them, with no distractions, however disgusting or violent, to relieve the long middle stretches of the dialectic on "An ox gores a cow". They wanted to get back to the Yeshivah Talmudical College, where at any rate there were over a hundred boys, games during break, occasional fights, simmering revolt, the interest of travelling by eleven different routes from Hackney and Dibley, and the vivid, noisy, crowded, smelly background of the East End. Eventually only Theodore was left. Then Rabbi Sborodinovich found a job in the provinces and the Racham was empty from one week-end to the next.

In due course, everybody grew older. Some died; Firmann died, Stannenberg died. "The boys", for better or for worse, went their own headstrong way. The congregation grew smaller, very small indeed. They no longer troubled to have electric light on Friday evenings at the Racham. The surviving elders sat by the flickering light of candles and muttered their old plaints. "Insanity, a madness has come upon the world ..." Brodkof left the district, it was growing slummy; not as it had been in the old days, when the carriages used to roll along Rutherstone Road. Somehow the Racham was kept open, until the war came and a bomb blew off the roof. The shattered house was pulled down; then nothing stood there at all, only a stretch of flat, levelled ground marked out for future development.

PART FOUR
STENHOLME
COLLEGE

1

THE SCHOLARSHIP, it seemed to David and his friends, was a reward for being clever. People were so fond of clever boys that they went out of their way to send them to a nice school, with a nice school cap and badge, and even gave them money, if they were poor, so that they should not have to go to the nice school with a hole in their trousers, or with leaky shoes, or wearing a jersey instead of a shirt, or carrying their books tied up with string, instead of in a nice seven-and-sixpenny satchel. That was how people felt towards clever boys, patting them on the head, pinching their cheeks, pointing them out admiringly, as they pointed out David's friend Theodore: "Top in every subject. Whew! And good at his Hebrew, too...." But heaven help you if you were not clever, especially if you were also poor. Then, no one cared what school you went to, no one bothered what sort of cap and badge it had. You could go to school with a hole in your trousers, with leaky shoes, you could carry your books tied up with string, or no books at all — it just didn't matter. You could do what you liked; who was interested, anyway?

David was very unsure of himself. Compared with some boys — boys who could not spell their own name, for instance, who could not do simple adding-up sums, and so on — he was clearly in the category of clever boys. But compared with others — not only with Theodore, who was a prodigy, or "genius", as they called him, but even with Sammy or Stanley, who were just ordinarily clever, David was nothing much at all. At sums, he was careless, erratic, and on the whole, mediocre. At essays — "compositions" — as befitted a future poet, he was quite good, though not at the top of the class. When it came to a neatly turned piece on "My favourite book", "My favourite film", "My favourite game", "School sports", "School holidays", and "Polar exploration", Theodore was still streets ahead.

David's uncertainty as to whether he belonged among the clever boys or among the undifferentiated mass lasted right up till the day when the results of the Scholarship were announced. They were all assembled in the Big Boys' Hall in Dibley Road School. David was standing next to a boy with the same name as himself: the other boy was called David Hirsch 1 and David himself was called David Hirsch 2. First the whole school recited morning prayers after the headmaster; then they sang a hymn.

After the hymn, the headmaster said:

"And now — aaaah! — I have here — aaaah! — the results of the Scholarship — maaaah!"

There was a faint stir of interest, culminating in a disturbance in the centre of the hall. The headmaster looked up sharply and said with quiet efficiency, and without the least bit of humming and hawing: "Will that boy go and stand outside my room immediately — I'll deal with him afterwards," he added to the rest of the school in an aside. "No, you! Yes, you — the boy in the brown jersey!" he shouted, as the boy in the brown jersey tried to push half a dozen boys round him into the position of guilt. Even now, when he had been specifically named, the boy in the brown jersey found it difficult to believe that he was not on the headmaster's side and assisting him in urging the culprit forward. Dazed and hesitating, with many a backward glance, pushed and jogged by busybodies when he paused too long, the boy in the brown jersey left the hall, and the headmaster cooed in his initial key of beatific benignity:

"It gives me great pleasure — muuuh! — to announce — haw! — the results — maaah! The school has — maw! — gained eight — uh! — Junior County Scholarships."

"Clap," whispered the master at the end of David's row. Someone clapped, but finding himself alone, stopped; he was followed by the master, and they all clapped, timidly at first, then loudly and vigorously, then in the slow, rhythmic unison which they knew was taboo. The headmaster raised his hand; had the occasion not called for a serene and joyful benignity and the long-planned, spontaneous concession of a half-holiday, he would have been angry.

"Stop clapping," urged the panic-stricken masters. They went on, in their slow, steady rhythm, but a few boys quavered, the clapping petered out, and the masters furiously noted the last boys to stop clapping.

The eight scholarship winners were announced: Theodore, of course, Sammy, Stanley, Elijah, and three others. The eighth name was David Hirsch. David Hirsch 1 and David Hirsch 2 jumped. They looked at each other, started forward, drew back, looked at each other again. David Hirsch 1 or 2? they asked the boys on either side, as if *they* knew.

"Come on," muttered the frantic master at the end of the row. David Hirsch 1 and David Hirsch 2 started forward again. The headmaster, seeing that there was some confusion, and used to having identical surnames and christian names in duplicate, or even triplicate, ran his finger down the list, turned over pages, consulted forms, and said, "David Hirsch 1". David was not sure, for the moment, whether he was David Hirsch 1 or 2.

"No, wait!" said the headmaster. "Wait!" He consulted his lists again, pulled out a register, and pondered. Then he said with finality, "David Hirsch 2. Yes, David Hirsch 2." David was thrown forward violently by the boys around him, and pushed and shoved along the row to take his place in the front of the hall with the other scholarship winners.

But ever afterwards he was not sure whether it was David Hirsch 1 or he himself who was the rightful winner of the eighth scholarship. Perhaps it was David Hirsch 1, and not he who should have learnt French, and written poems, and read text-books of philosophy? And perhaps it was he, and not David Hirsch 1, who should have been tailoring ladies' garments, and driving home in a car, and dealing with such correspondence as: "Send over one doz. lds. hmstchd. pltd. cstms. and please oblige J. Kramer"?

However, rightly or wrongly, David — David Hirsch 2 — took his place with the scholarship winners and received the rewards due to a clever boy. He was to go to a nice school, with a nice school cap and badge, and his parents received the appropriate money grant, so that he should not have to go to the nice school with a hole in his trousers, or with leaky shoes, or wearing a jersey instead of a shirt; and they bought him a nice seven-and-sixpenny satchel. People stopped him in the streets and patted him with approval. "Ooh! What a nice boy!" they said. "I hardly recognised you, you look so smart! Now you wear a nice smart shirt, with a nice smart tie, and a nice smart suit — mind you don't make it dirty! And what a beautiful satchel! I bet it cost a nice few shillings. What you got in it? Books, I bet, and inks and rulers. Dd! Dd! Wish I was clever like you."

As for David Hirsch 1, he ran around the streets as before. Who cared what happened to him, the blockhead!

2

AVID AND TWO OR THREE other scholarship winners decided to go, not to one of the local secondary and grammar schools, but to Stenholme College, in the far north of London. The school's high rate of success in examinations, said David's parents, and its tradition of catering for a large Jewish minority, would more than compensate for the daily bus journeys.

David and his companions had all read the *Magnet* and the *Gem,* and even the least imaginative saw in Stenholme College another Greyfriars and another St. Jim's, venerable, stately, situated in its own ancient grounds hallowed by immemorial tradition. They would not have been surprised to see local tradesmen touch their caps or to find that one of the boys was an earl and wore a monocle. Stenholme recreation ground, near the school, became a typical piece of rural England; the large open space enclosed by the front wall and the garages of an adjacent bus depot, and covered with an extraordinarily dusty mixture of sand and grit and pebbles, became the quad; while two arches underneath one of the garages became the cloisters.

David's first peep through the curtains of the Masters' Common Room was fairly reassuring. There they were, the species Magister Artium, as they had been described in the magazines, some of them knock-kneed, bow-legged, pot-bellied, with bulging eyes and protruding teeth, hee-hawing by the mantelpiece, smouldering pipe in hand; others clean-limbed, bronzed, athletic, frank. But who was this, a sort of raw, red, elderly gorilla with waxed moustaches prancing about in gym shorts and singlet? It was, David soon learnt, Sergeant-Major Battersby, the gym instructor and factotum of the Cadet Corps, a brave ex-soldier and a man of kind heart, but a trifle rough in his ways. The first time David spoke to him in his room off the gym, David said: "Pleassir —" Sergeant-Major

Battersby got up quite deliberately, folded his *Daily Mail,* lifted his spectacles from the ultimate fruit of his huge bulbous nose with about twenty-five deep holes and pits in it, put the spectacles in their case, blew out his purple cheeks and set his dewlaps quivering, then punched David smartly in the stomach. He followed up with a slap on each cheek, a neat tap on the jaw to set David's teeth rattling with his great broken paw, and finally a flat-handed blow and push on the stomach to send David flying backwards on to the floor of the gym.

"Git aht," he said; picked up his spectacles, replaced them on the ultimate fruit of his huge bulb, and resumed reading the *Daily Mail.*

He was rough in his ways, but not really bad-hearted. Once, when he set David as a punishment to raise the dumb-bells above his head five hundred times, he stopped David after two hundred.

"Go on," he said, " 'op it."

On another occasion David had to run round the front playground six times; the Sergeant-Major stopped him after four.

"All right," he said, "you c'n knock off nah."

When he had put David in detention for the rest of the term, he soon remitted the punishment to detention for the two following weeks only. And there was the touching moment when, after his laborious perusal of the paper through long-range spectacles resting distantly on the last ripe bulb of his nose, he gave David the *Daily Mail.*

" 'Ere y'are," he said, "wanna look a' the paper?"

David accepted with speed and gratitude; he was conscious of a great favour having been bestowed. One tended, he felt, to take newspapers too much for granted, simply because they cost a penny. Yet if one thought of the effort, the skill, the organisation involved in a single issue of a newspaper like the *Daily Mail:* the correspondents in all parts of the world; their ceaseless search for news; radio photography and the monotype machine; the day-and-night vigil in Fleet Street; the scrupulous care of subeditors; the vans and the trains waiting to speed the paper without an instant's delay to the shops ... all this for a penny. He read the first page of the *Daily Mail* through religiously, though he had already read most of the front page news in the *News Chronicle* at home. He had scarcely got half-way through page two, before Battersby said: "All right, Hirsch, you c'n "op it now."

"But I haven't finished the paper," said David.

Battersby flapped his dewlaps reflectively.

" 'Aven't you?" he said. "All right, you c'n take it "ome with you. No, "s all right," he insisted, as David protested in gratitude. " 'Op it."

In principle, he detested David. Firstly, David was a Jew, blatantly named Hirsch; secondly, David was a scholarship boy; thirdly, David belonged to that group which, all his life, both in the army and at school, had infuriated him — "the useless, spineless, boneless, brainless lot!" He sensed a member of this group immediately. He knew that David belonged to it on that very first occasion when he had punched David in the stomach. Nevertheless, a sort of — certainly not friendship, nor sympathy, nor even tolerance — but simply a sort of intimacy soon sprang up between them. Two people may be irreconcilable antagonists; after many years, they find that they have shared a great deal of experience. They do not, perhaps, hate each other any the less, but they realise that, for good or ill, they have lived in this world together at the same time and in the same place. They would feel lost without each other. Such was, in a very minor way, the relationship between Battersby and David during three or four years. They saw a lot of each other. Battersby kept David in after school, made him run round the playground, wait outside the Sergeant-Major's cubby-hole for a detention ticket. They did things together. They shifted the parallel bars, re-erected the horizontal bar. They moved the lockers, rolled up the mats. Sometimes they even chatted about Battersby's experiences in the army or about his poultry.

Not that there was any sentimentality between them. They were antagonists, that was understood. They loathed each other, that was understood. Battersby might once have given David the *Daily Mail,* and that was a piece of generosity for which David was grateful; it was a good turn which had to be repaid by making out a register or a couple of detention tickets, because Battersby had never got used to handling pens and was ashamed of being able to write only individual letters like an infant. But the debt having been repaid — and more than repaid, what with the parallel bars, and the lockers, and the mats as well — David felt that he had the right, and indeed the duty, to cause Battersby a certain amount of trouble.

Nature was cruel, David thought later, yet almost always, subtly and at her own unhurried pace, she redressed the balance towards justice and a universal equality; so that, to the oscillation of a billion individual tragedies, the dire cosmic scheme distributed itself into the ultimate, inconceivable harmony. As poets and moralists had pointed out, the worm turned the soil, grass grew, the bird ate the worm, the lamb ate the grass, men ate the bird, the lion ate the lamb, men died, lions died, they nourished the soil....

In the world of school, there seemed to be a complete disproportion between the powers of the schoolmaster and those of the schoolboy. The master had everything on his side. He had size, strength, and authority. He had the power to give lines, to set extra homework, to place the boy in detention, to keep him in after school. He knew how to isolate the boy from his fellows, to make him blush, to turn the eyes of the whole class on him in mockery. Behind the master stood the rest of the staff, the other masters, the lab. assistant, the school porter, and the headmaster. Behind the headmaster stood, if necessary, the police, and behind the police, the whole power of the state, the civil service, the armed forces, and the courts of law. On his side, what had the little schoolboy?

Nicknames? Notes from parents? Inky pellets catapulted at the master's head while he was bent over a book? Most of his counter-measures were futile and dangerous and failed to redress the balance of nature. No; essentially the schoolboy's weapon was the drawing-pin — unobtrusive, accidental, neat, tidy, procurable, and painful.

David was not present on the half-dozen occasions, spread over three or four years, when Battersby sat on his drawing-pins, but he was told that they were effective. The balance of nature was redressed and justice was done. David realised later that drawing-pins were dangerous and evil, and he would no longer positively have advised any schoolboy to use them; nevertheless, he would have advised schoolmasters to be careful how they threw their weight about, literally and metaphorically.

In summer, when swimming took the place of gym, other occasions for revenge presented themselves. Battersby was careless with his pullover, his absurd register with its meaningless hieroglyphs that he could neither read nor write, and with his spectacles — into the bath they went! David was placed under close arrest and lined up against the wall for summary execution; but eye-witness proof was lacking, and Battersby remembered that the Cadet Corps' dummy rifles could not be fired and that martial law was temporarily in abeyance.

Summer, in fact, was David's strong period in relation to Battersby, because David was an excellent swimmer, and having won several races, was less easily placed in the category, "useless, boneless, spineless, brainless, dozy lot". Moreover, he could not but play a prominent part in the games of water-polo; and when he got the ball, he threw it, not towards the opposing team's goal, but at Battersby's stomach, or into the water in such an accurate, skilful, and forceful way that it drenched Battersby and sent him spluttering back to the guard-room for his rifle — the ineffectual simulacrum of a rifle of which there were hundreds in the guard-room and which Battersby seized automatically in moments of rage and then flung aside disgustedly when he realised that the thing would not fire and that in any case the namby-pamby conventions of civilian life forbade the use of firearms against defenceless schoolboys.

Such — with some exaggeration, distortion, and pure fabrication, of course — were David's general relations with Battersby. And yet, David wondered, did the Sergeant-Major none the less eventually have some sort of affection for him? Perhaps, in an obscure way, he did. When, in David's fifth year, Battersby retired, he shook hands with David and said, gruffly and hoarsely:

"Goo'bye, Hirsch, and fer "eaven's sake, wake up! Wake yer ideas up, Hirsch, before it's too late!"

David certainly acquired in due course a respectful admiration and a kind of affection for the ex-soldier. Battersby must have been brave, and he was also true, his personality and appearance all of a piece, like those of an old war-horse or mastiff. Once or twice David even saw him smiling. The sight was queerly touching. David was by no means the only member of the "useless, bone-less, spineless, brainless, dozy lot"; and others, far more ill-used than David, sought, ineffectually, to revenge themselves with notes from parents and complaints to the headmaster, the governors, and the education author-ities. Most of these victims refused, logically and justly, to contribute to Battersby's retirement present; but in view of his special relationship with Battersby, David gave his mite to help speed the Sergeant-Major to his poultry-farm in Berkshire. The idea then crossed David's mind of the unfortunate lot of poultry. After all, human beings had god-like aspirations; all that they suffered had bearing on some magnificent end. In a way, they asked for trouble, they felt that there were things which made trouble worth while. But a chicken or a goose? What did a chicken ask out of life? Nothing. Sufficient if it was not eaten as an egg. More than enough if it was allowed to reach cock-hood and henhood and produce other chickens. Whatever happened to it, happened, apart from a few squawks. A

handful of crumbs satisfied its desires, a small coop shel-
tered it from the weather. Its only function was to be
eaten, at one stage or another in its precarious existence:
an unfortunate, fragile breed, and yet probably happy. It
was among these creatures that Sergeant-Major
Battersby, personification of all that was most carnivo-
rous in nature, had chosen to spend his retirement.

3

HOWEVER, IN PEEPING for the first time through the
curtains of the Masters' Common Room, David
was concerned only with the artistry of its inhab-
itants and whether they conformed to the types
encountered in the schoolboys' magazines.

He was more or less reassured. In a way, even Battersby
lived up to the Greyfriars tradition — there was always a
sergeant-major or two floating about the school in some
capacity or other — though it was probably not in order
that he should be beefing about the Masters' Common
Room. David made a place for Battersby too in the artistry
of the scene which presented itself through the curtains;
and followed his parents up to the hall, where the scholarship boys and their parents were to listen to an
introductory speech from the headmaster.

The headmaster made a very earnest speech about the
duties and responsibilities, as well as the privileges, of
attendance at Stenholme College. He emphasised particularly the need for house-spirit and team-spirit. The
speech, the hall in which it was delivered, the majestic
appearance of the headmaster were all that David could
have asked for; he was entering another Greyfriars.

At the end of the speech the headmaster's expression
suddenly changed. His severe judicial features broke into

what could only be described as a grin. The scholarship boys and their parents relaxed. They had not all understood the purport of the speech, but they knew that it dealt with serious and important matters, and they had listened gravely. Now it was over; the headmaster had grinned, and they grinned back. They congratulated each other. One mother unwrapped a packet of sandwiches which she had brought along for her son in case he should feel desperately hungry in the four hours between lunch and tea-time.

This grin, David afterwards found, was one of the headmaster's most pleasing characteristics. He had a sense of humour, Mr. Repston Fermoy. Years later David met him in the street.

"Mr. Repston Fermoy," said David, with a good deal of awe.

"Who are you?" he replied severely, and then grinned. "One of my former pupils, I suppose. Don't expect me to remember you. The trouble is, I've lived too long. I made no provision for living beyond eighty-five, at the outside … and here I am. It's deucedly awkward. Still, no doubt I shall manage to hang on till the end. Good luck to you, whoever you are."

But when he made his speech to the scholarship boys, he was a silver-haired, pink-faced youngster still in his seventies, with a muscular right arm developed through years of practice up in his study with the cane. "Cane the whole class!" he would say testily during the English lesson, and thereupon a class of thirty would file through his study, their trousers heavily padded with exercise-books and extra pairs of pants. "Bang!" went the cane on the trousers, the exercise-books, and the extra pairs of pants. Thin clouds of dust filled his study. "Bang!" again, and "bang!" Thirty times, just for one class. It was a remarkable feat for a man in his seventies.

After his speech and his grin, Mr. Repston Fermoy put on his mortar-board, and, his gown billowing behind him and all sails flying, scudded out of the hall through his special door and along the secret staircase which enabled him to be almost simultaneously on the platform and in the passage, to deliver a speech from the front and to shake hands or bark sternly from the rear. After he had reappeared swiftly and shaken hands with David's parents, David asked them what they made of some of the more difficult passages in the headmaster's address.

"It means you have to be a good boy," they replied.

David himself pondered the headmaster's references to the house-spirit, always very important in the boys' magazines. From the noticeboards outside the hall he discovered that there were four houses: Sennett's, Dean's, Layton's, and Hill's. And during his first few weeks at the school, he learnt that each house had an alliterative adjectival nickname: thus, "Soppy" Sennett's, "Dopey" Dean's, "Lousy" Layton's, three houses with pejorative adjectives, and "Happy" Hill's, the only house with a non-pejorative nickname, since no suitable alliterative adjective of disparagement had been discovered — though it was, in fact, the most dismal of houses, bottom at games and everything else, and certain, in the lot-drawing process whereby boys were distributed among the various houses, to receive the most melancholy, unhappy, and unfortunate newcomers.

David went into "Soppy" Sennett's and was ready to do his bit for the house. To begin with, he shouted "Dopey Dean's", "Lousy Layton's", and so on, at anybody who called out "Soppy Sennett's". He put his name down for the house sports teams. He had a successful fight with a boy smaller than himself in the back playground for calling his friend Sammy a Sennett's sissy. New boy that he was, he wanted to throw himself with enthusiasm — no, more than enthusiasm, fanatical loyalty, into this business of the house-spirit. But he very soon came to realise that it was quite factitious, there was absolutely no life in it. In the boys' magazines the house-spirit was terribly important, and only after desperate struggles did the hero's house become cock-house and win every games trophy and every scholarship and every school honour; whereas at Stenholme, no one really cared. At the end of the term, in the school magazine, house captains made their formal, half-hearted pleas, such as, "We must try and do better than this, Layton's", or, "Let's see if we can avoid being bottom at football this term, Hill's!" But no one cared, the boys scarcely even knew which busy form-master was nominally in charge of the house.

Instead of the pleasantly artificial divisions of the house-spirit, David found that there were other divisions, deriving from the everyday world of North London rather than from the delightfully significant and aesthetically satisfying world of the school magazines. The boys at Stenholme were split twice: into Jews and non-Jews, and into scholarship boys and paying boys. These divisions were not deep enough to be troublesome, but they were noticeably there. One or two members of the staff, for instance, drew attention in class to the difference between "some of you boys", "you lot", "some of you Jewish boys", "some of you scholarship boys from poorer homes" — or, more brutally, "Jew-boys" and "riff-raff" — between these two categories and the true-blue non-scholarship-holding non-Jews.

Battersby, of course, was the most outspoken of this small group on the staff, who were themselves as a rule former scholarship boys from country villages and provincial towns, though not, it was true, Jews. Battersby, though, he liked to boast of the brutal conditions in which he had himself grown up, was insistent on the distinction between "some o' you slum lot", "back-street boys", "some o' you scum o' the earth", and the rest. As for the Jews, Battersby usually referred to them as "Jew-boys", "Jew-lot" (or, under his breath, "Jew-bastards") and "foreigners"; but if in a good mood, he would vary between "the Yiddisher boys", "the Scotchmen" (or "the Irishmen" or "the Welshmen") and his favourite, "the -vitch's and -sky's".

There were, however, two anomalies which pained the more conservative masters, who could in no way be associated with Battersby and his claque: these two anomalies were the Jewish service and the "Fighting Onety-Oneth". When, a few minutes after nine, there was an immense shuffling of feet and it seemed as though the very building were moving towards the hall for morning prayers, the Jewish boys remained where they were, in their classrooms, for their own private services conducted by prefects and older boys. In theory all was well. The main service was conducted in the hall and the Jewish service was conducted in separate classrooms. But there was trouble: misbehaviour, unpunctuality, "messing about", and various abuses. As a result, a whole disciplinary system grew up round these Jewish services, with graded punishments and a special master to prowl about in the passage and make sudden raids on noisy rooms. Also, eventually, a weekly mass atonement was organised, whereby quite largish sums of money were collected from the Jewish boys for the purchase of books on Jewish subjects and objects of Jewish antiquarian or artistic interest to be presented to the school library and museum. Every month, therefore, a number of books of Jewish interest and various knick-knacks and objets d'art were presented to the Jewish section, which grew very rapidly. Before long, it occupied a whole wall full of shelves in the library and a substantial corner of the museum. Then it encroached on the Latin section, on the Greek, Sports and Games, Modern History, and French sections. In the most unexpected corners of the library, there would appear, say, *Some Notes on Talmudical Exegesis,* by Rabbi Dr Dirnfeld, M.A.; and the museum was munificently stocked with ritual candlesticks, miniature scrolls, and Jewish curios. The master in charge of the library was torn between his humorous teasing of the Jews and his love of, and greed for, more books and exhibits. "The Hebrews," he would write in the school magazine, "have again been the main contributors to the library and museum...."

97

Meanwhile, "Two-Gun Dixie" Macartney took over the disciplinary side of the Jewish services. Between the shouting for silence at the beginning; the collection of lines — "I must not be cheeky to a prefect during service", or "I must not be impudent", "I must not be impertinent"; the irruption of Two-Gun Dixie, his eyes flashing, his hybrid Anglo-Irish voice snarling, and his imaginary six-shooting Colts blazing; and the atonement collection of money at the end, there was little time left for prayer. One or two latecomers, such as David, sometimes tried to sneak into service unobserved, while Two-Gun Dixie was arguing things out with a boy further down the passage who had been sent out of the room for misbehaviour. But Dixie was like some sharp-eared animal of prey, whom the lightest of footsteps, the merest of creaks, would disturb. Rapping out to the victim whom he was already engaged in devouring, "Wait! Stay there! Don't move an inch!", he would whip round and tear off down the passage in pursuit of the latecomer, imaginary guns half out of their holsters, triggers cocked. Then, if the new victim had any spirit, an exciting chase began: down the main staircase, along the bottom corridor, round by the gym, up the sixth-form staircase, along the top corridor, down again, out to the lavatories, across the playground, round by the labs. — *not* past the guard-room, because that was where Battersby was beginning the first page of the *Daily Mail* — and quickly, with a last spurt, up the back staircase and into the classroom where the latecomer should all along have been sitting for service. If the prefect in charge was unco-operative, the game was up: but if the prefect co-operated, Two-Gun Dixie was foiled. He burst into the room, and, guns now out of their holsters, snarled:

"A buy" — that was how he pronounced "boy" — "has just entered this classroom!"

"Oh no, sir!"

Dixie looked at them with the cold sneer of hatred of the sheriff's man who knows that he is being framed but can do nothing about it. The expression on his face said distinctly:

"Yous guys think you're kinda smart, don't you...."

He slipped his guns into their holsters once again and backed out.

"O.K. You get away with it this time, but one o' these days you're gonna get what's comin' to yuh!"

The other major anomaly resulting from the existence of a large Jewish minority in the school was the "Fighting Onety-Oneth". The school had a Cadet Corps which trained mainly on Saturday mornings. Those Jewish boys whose religious observance forbade them to attend school on Saturdays therefore missed the greater part of their training. They were dumped into the least efficient of the school's "regiments", nicknamed the "Fighting Onety-Oneth". The "Fighting Onety-Oneth" made its presence felt in the mock-alarms that were held during normal school hours. However, mock-alarms took place only in summer and in fine weather.

The sun shone over the school playground. No sound broke the silence of morning lessons, except the drone of the masters' voices, the scratching of pens, the dropping of books, the whisperings and mutterings of illicit conversation, the revving of engines from the nearby bus depot, and the noise of a milk lorry crunching up the drive with six or seven hundred half-pint bottles of milk. Suddenly and unexpectedly — no clue had been given, other than Battersby's urgent waddling round each classroom and the casual remark that it need not startle them were there to be an alarm that morning — the thrilling call of the bugle sounded through the school corridors. Gaily and martially it rang out the tunes they knew and loved so well:

"Tara-tara-tarara!
Toora-toora-toorara!"

Action stations! England expects! ... They ran to the guard-room for their rifles. What a mêlée there was around the gun-racks! But no master could complain. This was no moment for red tape and petty discipline. Let us have our rifles, said the boys in effect, and show us the enemy! They tumbled out into the front playground. What splendid sunshine; how fresh and bright it was in the open air after having been cooped up in the classroom for over an hour.

The surface of the parade-ground was made up of sand, gravel, pebbles, stones, and dust. Very soon, six or seven hundred tramping, kicking feet were propelling thousands of stones at ground level. Above the heavier stones milled a six-inch layer of flying pebbles; then a stratum of gravel; and over all a thick, even cloud of dust. Visibility was almost nil. Instructions and communications were bawled incoherently by Battersby. Runners ran here and there with messages. Out of the fog loomed columns, squads, platoons, regiments, and stray boys.

The officer in charge, the brains, as it were, behind operations, was the Physics master, a scientifically minded soldier named Ainsley. The chief N.C.O. was, of course, Battersby, strutting around happily in a bowler hat. Ainsley had the brains, but no voice; Battersby had the voice, the necessary roar. Ainsley's syllables were transformed by the dust into an indeterminate sound — "hum!", or "humph!" at the end of a phrase. When the shuffling and tramping had diminished somewhat and it was presumed that they were as nearly in their places as they were ever likely to be, Ainsley began his precise, scientific instructions.

"Hum!"

They listened breathlessly, tying shoe-laces, straightening ties and caps.

"A-hum, a-hum, a-hum, humph-ah!"

Battersby translated into the vernacular.

"Git-up, git-up, it-all, it-all! Fawm in column of faws, haw-awm haws!"

"Form fours," they whispered to each other. They redistributed themselves.

"Hum-hum, humph-ah!"

"Bla-hoons, humber!" roared Battersby.

"Platoons number," they passed along the line. The cry was taken up.

"Number One Blaroon!"

"Number Doo!"

"Number Three!"

And so on, until the last platoon in the last regiment — the "Fighting Onety-Oneth" — was reached.

"Number Zigzdeen Blaroon!"

"All present and correct, sir!" shouted Battersby.

"Hum-ah, hum-ha, hum-ha, hum-ha, hum-ha," said Ainsley, chewing the cud about something. Then: "Hum-mm, humph!"

"Hoo-ooop, hipe!" was Battersby's rendering.

"Slope arms."

Out of chaos, order. Soon, the cloud-formation of dust formed regular patterns, with just here and there a little cyclone or whirlwind, a pocket of utterly hopeless disorder. There were mostly situated in or around the "Fighting Onety-Oneth".

The "Fighting Onety-Oneth" was a regiment of recalcitrants, as well as of the Jewish boys who would not parade on Saturdays. It was nothing but so much dead weight on the other regiments, who had somehow, in the course of the summer term, to prepare to pass beneath the inspection of a field-marshal on the final parade of the year. The "Fighting Onety-Oneth" was used as a dumping ground for rejects from the other regiments, and pacifist, communist, and anarchist propaganda was rife in the ranks. Little wonder, then, that it became increasingly irresponsible, derisive, unco-operative, and fractious, ruining the most ambitious projects and causing the headmaster, who alone could be seen by all rather than divined — upward visibility was good — to brandish his fist and wave his cane from his study window high above the parade-ground. Marching in line from one end of the parade-ground to the other, for instance, was a dream upon which Ainsley had set his heart. Observers near him reported that he raised his wooden sword and, bravely refusing to turn round and see what was happening, led the Cadet Corps' regiments broadside against the enemy.

"Keep line!" shouted Battersby. "Keep line! Heft! ... Heft! ... Heft! Hight! Heft! ... Heft! ... Heft! ... Heft! Hight! Heft! Hight! ... Heft! ... Heft! ..."

Before they had advanced a few paces past the guard-room, the broad front of the "Fighting Onety-Oneth" had begun to sag. Everyone could sense it, through the dust and the noise and the pandemonium. Where *was* the centre of the "Fighting Onety-Oneth"? Had it even started out yet? Demoralisation spread to the third regiment, and eventually reached the first. Flanks tapered off and thinned out. Laggers rushed forward. Those in advance lagged. Bulges surged and billowed, forward and outward, backward and inward. Ainsley kept marching, marching, onward, onward, his sword upraised, with never a glance behind. Battersby hit a boy in the second regiment. The headmaster rattled the window of his study to draw attention to his cane. Ainsley reached the end of the parade-ground with a section of the first regiment. In sudden rushes, or weary, never-say-die ploddings, the others arrived. Lastly, ingloriously, talking animatedly among themselves about pacifism, communism, and anarchism, some with their rifles at the trail, some with their rifles tucked comfortably under their arms, came the "Fighting Onety-Oneth". The operation was ruined.

Later, when real operations began, the "Fighting Onety-Oneth" took part, along with the other regiments. The recalcitrants, too, wore uniforms and held real rifles.... For the duration of the war the school was transferred to Wales. Long before then, the Cadet Corps had reduced its numbers and given up the practice of mock-alarms. But the parade-ground became the scene of warlike activity for several years. Manoeuvres of an unprecedented and quite unorthodox kind were held, and dangerous expeditions under enemy fire were organised. From the guard-room, first-aid men rushed to their ambulances, and beneath the long beams of searchlights fire engines clanged down the drive and through the streets of North London. Near the walls of the bus depot, over the stretch of sand, stones, pebbles, dust, and gravel where the "Fighting Onety-Oneth" had stood permanently at ease, and where pacifist, communist, and anarchist propaganda had been rife, over that abandoned terrain, peopled only in memory, lay a static water-tank.

PART FIVE
UNCLE JAKE

1

DAVID SLEPT in the front room on the ground floor. This room was, quite rightly, not called the sitting-room, the parlour, the lounge, or the drawing-room, because it was none of those things. Instead it was called, accurately, the front room or the best room. In order to transform it from the front room into the best room, the Hirsches had to remove or conceal thoroughly all signs of David's having slept there. The bedclothes were carried en masse into the next room, the put-u-up was folded with a great twanging and jangling of springs, cushions were disposed over it with a suggestion of carelessness, an odd pyjama jacket or used pair of socks was bundled into a drawer, and with a final, backward glance of inspection — always feeling that something, perhaps something really *awful,* had been left in the dead centre of the room — they prepared to admit their guests into the best room.

"Who," David wondered, "invented the put-u-up?" The idea of such a contraption having been conceived, translating it into fact must not have been difficult. But how did the idea come to be conceived? What sort of a man, staring at his bed, was driven to speculate on the possibility of tipping it end up, collapsing it in on itself, and stuffing it out of sight into a semblance of couch? A bed, which of all things ought to represent horizontal permanence, tranquillity, and repose!

Adult guests were not too bad, because they came in the evening, when, however late David slept, he was well

104

clear of the put-u-up and the front room. The real bane of his life was the arrival of his father's pupils for their Hebrew lesson on Sunday morning. At first there were only two of them. Later they grew to be a dozen or more. It did not take them long to find out that the best room, in which they received their lesson and before entering which they were asked to wipe their feet, was also David's bedroom. The first to arrive peered in through the window and said to each other:

"David's not up yet. Let's have a game of football."

They began to dribble a ball up and down the quiet street. Others arrived; they tossed for sides, made goals of lamp-posts and heaps of overcoats, occasionally broke a window. Neighbours complained. It was all David's fault for sleeping late.

However, he came to realise how lucky he was to have a bedroom at all, with a comfortable bed, even if it was a put-u-up, plenty of space and air, and undisturbed possession during the night and for six mornings in the week. He came to realise his good fortune by comparing it with the predicament of Uncle Jake.

Late one night David was awakened by a tapping at the window and the noise of twigs crackling on the low bushes of the front garden. Someone was moving about; there was the ticking sound of a bicycle chain being spun backwards, then a further gentle tapping at the window. He had at first been alarmed, but on hearing little noises connected with a bicycle, he was reassured, feeling certain that Uncle Jake was around. Uncle Jake was always wheeling, repairing, hiding, locking up, or dashing out to keep an eye on the bicycle which was his major possession and indispensable both to his livelihood and his mode of living. Illogically, but correctly, David therefore deduced that where there was the sound of a bicycle chain, Uncle Jake was not far away.

David crept out of bed and opened the window.

"Hullo," he whispered. "Is that Jake?"

"Yes," replied Jake. "Keep the window open, I want to

105

come in."

He spun the chain of his bicycle backwards through a few revolutions, snapped a lock to, and climbed through the window.

"Why didn't you let me open the door?" said David.

"I don't want anyone to know I'm here."

Jake scrambled in and began to speak with some agitation.

"Listen, David," he said. "You don't understand these things yet, but I've got nowhere to sleep. Do you think you could make room for me in your bed? I wouldn't ask you to do this, except that I've got nowhere to go. And I must get some sleep, or I shan't be able to carry on with my work and my studies."

"Of course," said David, "hop in."

Uncle Jake hopped in and after addressing his nephew at length on the necessity for education, socialism, and liberty, fell into a deep sleep, broken very occasionally by bouts of uneasy snoring. When David awoke in the morning, he was gone.

During the day David might see Uncle Jake flying along on his bicycle, too busy to stop, a bundle of library books and notebooks and a bag full of possessions strapped to his back; and at night there would be a slightly agitated tap on the window, a long address on psychology, the principles of education, and the future of civilisation, and then sleep. But after a time David left the window open for his uncle: so that he often did not know whether Jake had been during the night or not.

Uncle Jake was the "bad lad" of the family. Not that he ever drank, like the synagogue porter, or had ever been caught buying stolen goods, like the one time vice-president of a neighbouring synagogue; nor did he gamble at the dogs, like the habitués of the barbers' shops, or jilt his betrothed for another with a larger dowry, like any sensibly wicked young man who frequented Saturday-evening dances. No, Uncle Jake had none of these reasonable and more or less acceptable vices — instead, he "ran after madness". People

106

saw him pedalling about on his bicycle at all hours of the day and night, riding furiously here and there — and what for? For madness! In order to read library books and go to meetings, in order to study intermittently and wear open-necked shirts — in a word, in order to waste his life away.

He was irreligious: a philosophical "epicurean", infinitely worse than those who neglected religion simply because the flesh was weak. Almost as bad as his irreligion was his lack of interest in marrying some "nice Yiddisher girl". He not only refused to negotiate with the matchmakers, but declined invitations to attend Saturday-evening dances, where "he would have enjoyed himself, the fool!" with the sandwiches, jollity, Paul Joneses, and twilit waltzes.... If the matchmakers and dance-club secretaries spoke to him at all, it was only out of pure goodness of heart, since who would look at him in his open-necked shirt and his grey-flannel trousers? In summer, he would not even have been allowed into the dances, since he wore shorts. "For why? For because he can't affuder a long peh truzzers!" said old Granny Dubkin, the Rutherstone Road matchmaker. "A job he hasn't got! Money he hasn't got! Only a bicycle he's got! And books from the library he's got!..." David could have told her that even a bicycle he hadn't got, but was paying off for on a prolonged hire-purchase scheme which involved continual threats of confiscation and last warnings to half-a-dozen addresses from which he had been evicted on the very first occasion when a week's rent in advance had fallen due and he had been unable to pay by midday.

Uncle Jake was accounted a "bad lad" and a guilty taciturnity overcame the solvent body of the family whenever he was so hungry and lacking in taste as to enter a kitchen where they were all gathered. But for David, in later years, Jake's virtues were visible in all their noble humility, their stubborn modesty, their devious, often uncomprehending tenacity of faith. Heroic Jake! thought David. North London Prometheus! Your entrails were torn out by sixteen-stone landladies and your ordeal derided by the wives of fishmongers! Stepson of England, on your mortgaged bicycle, you pedalled along the impossible roads of escape, but endlessly, in all directions the grey slums and suburbs stretched....

2

I N THE RETROSPECT of later years, David came to the conclusion that if the pleasures of the intellect are deepest and most abiding, Uncle Jake was a life-long voluptuary. With what delight Jake adduced analogies, laid down and discarded hypotheses, built up and abandoned systems, played chords and harmonies of fact like a pianist tapping the keyboard of his special, easeful instrument. And little wonder that, taken up in the pursuit of intellectual pleasure, he had no capacity for pulling levers on a machine, or serving behind a shop-counter, or following any of the occupations he might have been expected to follow. For such unheeding dissipation a man must be prepared to suffer; and Uncle Jake was prepared to suffer, thereby rendering his position as a voluptuary and individualist impregnable.

Thus, on an occasion shortly after he had left school when he almost knocked himself unconscious against a lamp-post, he did not complain or make a fuss: instead, he studied his injuries and pointed out their peculiarities. Apparently, he was running along in the dark. Why he was running, David did not discover, though he felt pretty sure there was no special reason. Probably Jake was just jogging along at a fastish trot. Perhaps, in the manner of the physical-cultural enthusiasts in whom Hackney abounded, he believed in running at all times, held that running, and running alone, produced certain virtues and powers, mental as well as physical — like the rather short young man round the corner, a medical student, who walked along in springy six-foot strides and with his chest pushed well out. Each step was an achievement and he was, and looked, proud of it. People felt like clapping as he passed — "Keep it up! Keep it up!" Or like — though this was to bring the comparison into altogether too questionable a territory — Kitzlavski's father, who advocated counting four as one breathed in and four as one breathed out, at every breath, as a means both of prolonging life indefinitely and of giving it the balance necessary for securing an entry into a strictly Jewish heaven when one did die.

At any rate, Uncle Jake was running along the street on a dark night when he ran into a lamp-post. Presumably this part of the street was unlit; otherwise, in spite of the fact that he was lost in thought at the time, he would surely have seen the lamp-post. But he did not, and he was dazed and badly bruised when he tottered into the Levys' kitchen, his spectacles smashed, his face white and spattered with blood, and his forehead swelling up into two enormous bumps. It was these bumps which interested Jake most.

"Have you ever considered," he said to David, as the only one young enough to retain a detached curiosity, "how odd it is that a blow on the head should produce a bump? If you hit a piece of wood" — he hit the chair — "does it swell up into a bump? If you bang a kettle" — he banged the kettle — "does anything happen? No. Only if you bang the human head —"

He picked up a heavy spoon, as though to bang his head, but Granny Dubkin, who happened to be in the room, snatched it from his hand, crying: "Oy! The knock has upset his mind!"

"Only if you bang the human head," continued Uncle Jake with enthusiasm and real joy, "do you produce a bump. Tomorrow we must go to the library and find out why...."

Granny Dubkin, in subsequent moments of pique, when her matchmaking offers had been ignored, used to maintain that this knock on the head had permanently affected Uncle Jake's reason. She used to point to his forehead, shake her own head in a gesture of immemorial sorrow, and say: "The bump has gone, but not the crunk!" Alternatively, she said that he had always been the same, only since the bump he was more so — "From the madness came the bump — head in the other world, not looking where he's going, running like a lunatic. Who run? Lunatics run. I run? Mr. Levy runs? The rabbi runs? But Jake runs! His madness is a crunk. And the crunk brought another crunk. On the head, that's where a person's sense is. And now it's too late. What can one do?" she concluded resignedly.

The family did not accept Granny Dubkin's thesis entirely, but all agreed — indeed, it was an undeniable fact — that it was not until after his collision with the lamp-post that Jake really "turned".

Characteristically, "turning" began with bouts of intense religiousness and Jewish patriotism. Jake became more religious than anyone else — "too much is also no good" — and too enthusiastic in his studies of the Talmud. He had been apprenticed in the tailoring trade, but insisted on giving up work in order to study the Talmud all day at the Yeshivah Talmudical College. In the tailoring trade he was already earning 7s. 6d. for a sixty-hour week, which, if not a good wage, was at any rate a wage, and enabled him to pay his way in the Levy household. He had, therefore, to look for alternative means of acquiring money. The course had been marked out by generations of talmudical students: it consisted firstly in applying for direct assistance from college and synagogue authorities, and secondly in doing all sorts of free-lance religious work, such as chanting a portion of the Bible on Saturdays, coaching boys to chant their portion on their thirteenth birthdays, giving Hebrew lessons, and so on.

On the surface, to give up a fine future in the tailoring

trade in order to study the Talmud was a praiseworthy gesture, and the college authorities could not but allow Jake a small grant of five shillings a week, whatever their unspoken misgivings about the suddenness and intensity of Jake's religious inspiration. Likewise, although Jake had a rather croaky singing voice, he had little difficulty in securing free-lance work as a chanter of the Bible, since croaky singing voices were highly considered among connoisseurs of Bible-chanting. Jake found himself earning more as a student of the Talmud than an apprentice in the tailoring trade. All would have been well if he had stuck to what he was doing. How often that comment was applicable! All would have been well if he had stuck to what he was doing.... But no sooner was he settled down at the college and doing his freelance work, earning ten-and-six, twelve-and-six — fifteen-and-six a week! — than ideas began to enter his head.

The elders of the synagogue had seen trouble coming with Jake ever since he had quit tailoring. "A tailor is a tailor and a rabbi is a rabbi. That a rabbi should become a tailor, is that good? That a tailor should become a rabbi, can that also be good?" What was more, when he was most enthusiastic about studying the Talmud and becoming a rabbi, Jake was not satisfied just with attending at the Yeshivah Talmudical College. He had to go and do "research" at various libraries in the West End, comparing the Babylonian and the Palestinian Talmuds, trying somehow to fit the Talmud harmoniously — as though it were an authoritative modern work prepared under the auspices of the Oxford University Press and edited by an unimpeachable scholar years ahead of his time called God — into the overall historical picture of the ancient world.

"Resetch!" snorted the elders of the synagogue. "What is that, something to eat?" For two thousand years, the holiest and most learned rabbis — some of them so holy and learned that their wisdom and sanctity were not conceivable to the modern mind — for two thousand years such men had got along without "resetch". And now a

whippersnapper like Jake, a shnip, a nobody, wasn't satisfied, but had to go to the West End, did you ever hear,
to the West End, to do "resetch".

But in any case, "resetch", like Jake's other peculiarities,
was simply a factor in the process of "turning". The elders
had only to wait, and everyone would see how right they
were.

They had not long to wait. After about a year at the
Yeshivah Talmudical College, quite suddenly, in the
middle of the summer, Jake "turned". He came into the
house through the back garden wheeling a brand-new
bike. It ticked confidently to a stop and Jake entered,
whistling quietly and peacefully. A rucksack was
strapped to his back and he wore, instead of the usual
trilby-hat, a beret.

"You've bought a bike? And what's the rucksack for?"
asked David's aunts.

"I'm off tomorrow," he said casually.

"What, to camp?" David's aunts were referring to the
religious students' camp, where Jake had spent his holiday the previous year. "Thought it wasn't till next week."

"No," said Jake, "I'm going round the country working
on farms and things."

"No jokes, are you really going tomorrow?"

"Yes."

"Where, to camp?"

"No, round the country, working on farms and things."

And so on for some time; until the family realised that
the mystical cord which, for all his eccentricities, bound
Jake to them and to all that was reasonable and normal,
had snapped, cruelly, inexplicably, and unnecessarily.
Jake was, voluntarily and alone, descending to the lowest
section of society; he was going to become a homeless
casual labourer, a tramp, a criminal even. A young man
who had no money, no job, no home, no wife, no friends,
was, in essence, a criminal. More than in essence: in fact
— where had he got that bicycle from?

Jake left home and never returned to live, though he

did drop in from time to time to see how everyone was getting on and have a cup of tea and "a bite". And what bites! Immense, devouring, terrible! They were not bites, they were seizures, engulfments. Remembering them David was able to recognise at a glance the difference between a man who is hungry, who has worked up an appetite since breakfast, and a man who is chronically hungry, who has built up an appetite in weeks and months. Uncle Jake was no believer in eating; he rather despised it and the demands it made on a man. Sipping a cup of tea he spoke of educational psychology, while a steaming plateful of meat and potatoes was set in front of him. Suddenly, in mid-sentence, he broke off. The cup clashed on to the saucer, half-spilling its remaining contents. He fell upon the food and for a long time said not another word.

3

A T THE end of the summer Uncle Jake returned from the country, took a room in the district, and became a student. He remained a student, on and off, officially or unofficially, for the next fifteen years. It took him four years to matriculate, six years to pass the intermediate examination, and five years to pass the final examination. If this seemed a long time, the conditions in which he worked had to be borne in mind.

From time to time, as at the end of that first summer when he "worked on farms and things", he collected together a few pounds and took a room. He bought notebooks, borrowed text-books from the libraries of three or four boroughs, paid off instalments on his bicycle, and began to study, hoping to live by doing odd jobs and, later, giving lessons. His money ran out, the instalments on his bicycle accumulated, and he was evicted from his room, sometimes after all his possessions except the bicycle had been impounded. Then, for weeks or months, he led a desperate existence. He slept where he could: at one period with David, at other periods with friends or very distant relatives. The latter were often, to begin with, only partly aware of his homeless existence, and then needed time to bring their relationship to the point where he was barred from the house except, say, at lunch-time on a recognised day of the week. His clothes deteriorated, his credit exhausted itself entirely. He was driven to rehabilitate himself by getting a job, even though this meant suspending his studies. He thought that he would be able to maintain himself, buy clothes, pay off his debts, and save up some money by working very hard for three or four months. In practice, in those decades of unemployment, he found the greatest difficulty in securing a menial and poorly-paid job in the tailoring trade. For three or four months he was still scarcely able to maintain himself. Debts could not possibly be paid, apart from an instalment or two on the bicycle to save it from confiscation, and he might never have resumed his studies had he not continually got the sack and received the dole and even lower benefits, which had the one virtue, from Jake's point of view, of bestowing leisure in which to study. In the summer, by "working on farms and things", and saving rent by sleeping, perhaps, in a barn, or in a tattered tent which he at some point acquired, he managed to save a little money and return to North London with renewed hope and purpose.

For matriculation he had no teachers whatsoever, and he was always dependent on the libraries for text-books, for the most essential of which there was lively competition from other students similarly placed. On the first occasion when he was ready to enter for the examination he could not scrape together the entrance fee. Useless to try and borrow it; no one would believe that he really wanted the money for that purpose. Later, when he did

114

finally enter, he failed. In such circumstances, that he passed at all after only four years, and at his second attempt, was no small achievement.

After matriculation, he found it a little easier to obtain occasional work as a coach, and his financial position improved very slightly. On the other hand, he had to combine lectures with his lessons and odd jobs and give time to political and social activity in the students' clubs of the North London College, a college of London University where, for the first term of each session, three years running, he became an internal student. Unable, until his fourth year, to find the second and third terms' fees, he had to leave and start again the following session. Studying for the examination externally would have saved him a great deal of money, but he was determined to be a real student, an internal student, and take a good degree. Fees, politics, movements, and all the usual troubles, including the fact that the bicycle was beginning to feel the effects of hard usage and need constant repair — it was once again not surprising that six years and two attempts were necessary for Jake to pass the intermediate examination. And when he began to study for the final examination, politics and social activity were superseded by his work on a book, "the novel".

After the intermediate examination, Jake was able to obtain a concession from the college authorities whereby most of his fees were remitted until after he had graduated, when he was to pay them back in monthly instalments — a sort of hire-purchase scheme for a degree, similar to that by which he had secured his bicycle. This ought to have eased the pressure on his existence a little and enabled him to study more peacefully. In addition, he gave up politics and was thereby freed from the demands made on his time by meetings, rallies, discussions, debates, circles, and newspaper-selling. But in fact the final phase of his studies was almost as impossible as the earlier phases. Politics was replaced by innumerable drafts of "the novel". By this time he had completely severed his connection with tailoring and could no longer obtain even the last remnant of the most niggardly dole or benefit which he had previously extorted from his natural enemies, the clerks at the Hackney Labour Exchange. He was entirely dependent on tutoring, which necessitated, when he was fortunate enough to have a sufficiency of pupils, incessant and daylong travelling between the North London College, the Hackney, Stoke Newington, Dibley, Whitechapel, and Bethnal Green public libraries, and Bow, Victoria Park, Clapton, Stamford Hill, Tottenham, Highgate, Hornsey, Finchley, and Golders Green (that promised land of the private tutor). All this without his bicycle; because the glittering, ticking, closely-guarded, heavily-mortgaged machine of five or ten years before was now a broken-down, finally paid-off, carelessly left-about, rusty hulk, which, reduced to scrap, was given to David as a present. Without the bicycle Uncle Jake was not the same. The wear and tear of life was beginning to tell upon him. It was one thing for David to see a preoccupied, determined, self-willed Jake pedalling furiously, too busy to stop, from pupil to pupil and from library to library, astride his bicycle; and another to see a slight, shortish man in an old mackintosh, whom David scarcely recognised among other shortish men in old mackintoshes, travelling slowly and on foot through the same urban landscape which unlit by youth and enthusiasm, was visibly grey and depressed.

The hulk of the bicycle was given to David, and on it he came as near to losing his life as he had ever done. In spite of warnings from Jake and others, he insisted on riding it, although it had no brakes, no lights, a shaky handlebar, a bent frame, and both inner tubes in slow puncture, which meant that at the best he had to get off every half-an-hour and pump them up. But it was not so much the bicycle which brought him near to death as his own ignorance and the folly of the authorities in allowing anyone, no matter how inexperienced or scatterbrained, to take to the road, without licence or test, on no matter how unroadworthy a machine. Uncle Jake's discarded hulk was sufficient of a menace on the roads of Hackney. But when in addition its rider, David, was under the suicidal delusion — until one day he heard the brakes of a car, as a result, screech agonisingly to a halt and saw the car spin round full circle in order to avoid killing him — that holding out his right arm indicated the intention of turning to the left, then it was clear that only the personal intervention, so often afterwards called for and mercifully granted, of his tutelary angel, "the angel who watches over the boys", averted his early death.

A policeman, not an angel, saved his friend Theodore, who used to borrow the bicycle, sometimes without permission — what youthful obsession must have held Theodore in its grip to induce him to make off with that wreck! He was coasting down a hill on the way to Chingford, without brakes, of course. If anyone had set Theodore a question in an examination — "Can a bicycle without brakes, travelling downhill, be pulled up when a policeman holds out his arm to halt the traffic?" — Theodore would undoubtedly have given the correct answer, "No", as he gave the correct answer to every question in every examination he ever sat for. Theodore knew the answer abstractly, but not in life itself. Consequently, coasting gently downhill on the way to Chingford, he had no idea what to do when a policeman held out his arm to stop the traffic, and he steered Uncle Jake's bicycle into the policeman's back. Fortunately, he could not have been going very fast, and the policeman was solid, so little damage was done. But the policeman instructed Theodore to wheel the dangerous hulk home, and threatened him with Borstal if it were ever seen on the road again.

Finally David sold it for fourpence in the stolen bicycle mart in Club Row, Bethnal Green, in part exchange for a newly-painted, half-a-crown racing cycle which looked splendid. The only condition of sale was that he should not ride the "almost new" racer in Club Row itself, as "that wouldn't look good". David realised why when he turned the corner and mounted, because the "almost new" racer collapsed and disintegrated beneath him, and one wheel, the only sound part of the cycle, went bowling along the road on its own. He did not attempt to chase it, nor to collect the remnants of the racer which lay strewn about the gutter, but bolted off as fast as he could and caught a bus home, after which time he took no further interest in bicycles.

4

DURING HIS last ten years at the North London College, Uncle Jake rarely came to visit the family. Nevertheless, David saw him fairly often in the street. Sometimes, in the days of the bicycle, he rode slowly alongside the kerb and David trotted along with him to his latest lodgings and listened to him reciting poetry or discussing philosophy. David could always tell whether he was in love or not, because when he was in love, his chief interest was poetry, out of love, philosophy; and David could tell with whom he was in love by the political movement he was in. The Zionist movement meant Sadie; the Communist Party, Rose; the Labour Party, Joan; the I.L.P., Phyllis; and the Anarchists, Betty. Of course, such deductions were only the silly over-simplifications of childhood. Actually, Uncle Jake's progress from Zionism to anarchism and beyond involved years of reflection, study, and experience, and the interest he took in Sadie, Rose, Joan, Phyllis and Betty was quite independent of his serious political development. Nevertheless, as a working guide for David's childish curiosity, the coupling of Jake's emotional and political life seemed to be unfailingly accurate. It explained for David the hesitancy in Jake's world outlook at the time when he oscillated between the Zionist movement and the Labour Party; likewise his sudden conversion to the I.L.P., and so on.

David was a child and did not understand politics. At the age of eleven or twelve, he had no notion that the activities which he observed in one or two houses and converted shops in Hackney might alter people's lives for better or for worse. He was a being "for whom the visible world existed", and the impressions which in Uncle Jake's company he received of the Dibley branches of political parties were therefore purely local, immediate, sensory.

However, he did receive such impressions. Uncle Jake took him, at least once or twice, as a matter of principle, to each of the parties which he himself joined in turn. If there was one thing Jake believed in more than another it was education in the broadest sense. There could never be enough of it and it could never begin too early. It could admit no reticences and no divisions between the academic and the non-academic, the adult and the juvenile. In spite of occasional raised eyebrows and even titters, he made a point of taking his nephew to the Zionists, the Labour Party, the communists, the anarchists, and the I.L.P. David's education could not be neglected.

Whatever their value at such an early age, these explorations delighted David, and he looked forward eagerly to any signs of a change in Uncle Jake's political views with its promise of an ensuing change of scene. Uncle Jake was the perfect uncle, neither remotely adult, nor falsely juvenile, but just delightfully, seriously, and absurdly avuncular. David watched with wide-eyed curiosity Uncle Jake's political quest and the sentimental quest seemingly associated with it. For his own childish reasons, he participated in Jake's enthusiasms and shared his disappointments.

The Zionist movement was Uncle Jake's first love, and that had a great deal of youth and poetry about it.

Everyone wore shorts and open-necked shirts, even in mid-winter. They hated staying indoors; the house which was their headquarters was nothing but a thoroughfare to the garden, where the young Zionists sat round a bonfire which burned more or less continuously throughout the year. In spite of their open-necked shirts and shorts, and even bathing costumes, they were not cold. On the contrary, their faces were red and they perspired gaily. For one thing there was the bonfire, and for another they hardly stopped dancing a vigorous, leg-kicking dance called the Horroh. No sooner had they sunk panting round the bonfire after their latest bout, than someone who had been waiting for the opportunity to be the first to start a dance and shout the ritual cries, leapt up and called, *"Horroh!"* There could be no holding back. They were all up on their feet again, swinging and kicking in a circle round the bonfire. They began at a moderate pace, singing in Hebrew:

"Hovvoh, noggilloo *hov*voh, noggilloo *hov*voh, noggilloo *vey*-ismech*oo*!"

Then they worked up speed, and they panted:

"Hovvoh nerunnenoh, hovvoh nerunnenoh, hov*voh*, hov*voh*, *ner*unnenoh — *oh*!

"Hovvoh nerunnenoh, hovvoh nerunnenoh, hov*voh*, hov*voh*, nerunnen*oh*!"

After this the dance began to get out of hand. Some wanted to run faster than ever, others were quite out of breath. Tall, lanky young men fell over small dumpy girls, who refused to be disconcerted. The core of the young Zionist movement appeared to consist of these small, dumpy girls, whose spirit nothing could daunt. Cheerful, hardworking, capable, sincere, completely loyal, they were the first up and the last down. They would have collapsed rather than break the circle. To steady the rhythm they began a fast, even chant:

"Yooluyluy, yooluyluy, yooluh-yooluh-yooluyluy, yooluy-luh-yooluy-luh-*yoo*yooluyluyluy!" The tempo quickened and became once again more erratic, Uncle

Jake's spectacles fell off, and every time he moved round in the circle to where they had fallen and remained miraculously unbroken, he kicked them out of the dancers' path towards the bonfire. One kick landed them almost among the burning lumps of wood. He had to break the circle to rescue them. The circle immediately re-formed, and with Uncle Jake as a kind of sacrificial victim beside the flames, strange desert cries and responses were uttered.

"Ushkariah!" yelled the person who had started the dance.

"Fantaziah!" yelled the dancers.

"Fantaziah!" came the counter-call.

"Ushkariah!" was the response.

"Ushkara!"

"Fantala!"

"Fantala!"

"Ushkarah!"

Then the original song was begun again, but faster, wilder, the dancers kicking and panting and stamping with mad gaiety, and Uncle Jake grinning amiably and patiently through reinstated spectacles as he was jostled into the bonfire.

"Hovvoh, noggilloo hovvoh...!" — the whole punctuated with yells of "Ushkariah! Ushkara! Fantala!"

"At any rate," said passers-by who watched over the back-wall — though not the neighbours, who spoke of complaining to the police — "at any rate, they're enjoying themselves...."

5

THE SAME, David thought, could not be said of the East Dibley Labour Party. The secretary and his assistants at local headquarters pottered around gloomily, sucking unlit pipes or yellowing cigarette-butts.

"Seen Mr. Jenkins?"

"No."

"Mr. Williams turned up?"

"No."

Silence: pipes were taken out, shaken, and replaced, cigarette-butts swivelled with dextrous tongue-flicking.

"Mrs. Feingold said she was coming."

"Oh?"

"So did Miss Rogers."

"Hm?"

Silence: pipes and cigarette-butts as before.

"Did you hear from Jacobs?"

"No."

"Williams written?"

"No."

Politics seemed to be taboo. David noticed the spitting into corners and the raised eyebrows when Uncle Jake mentioned a piece of news he had read in that morning's *Daily Herald*. The regular conversation was hastily resumed.

"Seen Johnson?"

"Seen Ferguson?"

If Uncle Jake and his nephew wanted to make themselves useful, they could address envelopes — thousands of them. The walls were lined with envelopes.

Inconsequentially observant, David noticed recurring features at each local headquarters of the political parties: in particular, a large, mouldering poster, showing the familiar smile of a little girl standing with her back to a garden wall, while her younger brother played at her feet with a bucket and spade. David thought he recognised the little girl and her brother. They closely resembled the pair who played on the poster hanging in the Zionist head-quarters. Having already seen them twice, he was subsequently not surprised to meet them again in the course of his explorations with Uncle Jake. Sure enough, they turned up at the offices of the Communist Party. The liberals and conservatives, he discovered at election-time, also displayed a very similar boy and girl on one set of their posters. Here, in the Labour Party headquarters, they were labelled: "Labour Gets Things Done".

By way of contrast to the Labour Party offices, the Communist Party headquarters, under the energetic command of Nobby Hyams, seemed to vibrate with dynamism. The revolution, David felt, might take place the very next morning. Messages passed to and fro, the drama group went about their rehearsals at the double, new classes and sections were organised daily — poetry, needlework, elocution, French, German, Spanish, Russian, Hebrew, history, logic, chess, boxing, all-in wrestling, public speaking — recruits were enrolled and expelled before you could say Jack Robinson.

David found the Young Communist Party romantic and exciting and was thrilled on the few occasions when Uncle Jake took him to their underground headquarters in the cellars of a disused synagogue. Uncle Jake once left David standing in the passage while he himself ham-mered out a point with some comrades in the committee-room. No one took any notice of the twelve-year-old. David strolled into the office and idly turned the pages of a book lying on the table. A letter lay open beside the book. One sentence in it caught his eye; it referred to Uncle Jake. "He has deviationist tendencies; his charac-ter is weak and he needs watching."

David was not surprised, therefore, when Uncle Jake was expelled shortly afterwards. The showdown came during a session of the poetry class which Uncle Jake con-ducted. He recited stanzas and invited discussion. His eyes on Rose, he said:

"Shall we roam, my love, by the twilit foam,
Where the waves are dancing bright?
Oh, I'll whisper there, in the cool night air,
What I dare not in broad daylight!..."

Meanwhile, Nobby Hyams had entered and stood at the back of the cellar.

"That is an adolescent trifle by Shelley," said Jake, "a charming and musical little piece, admirably suited to —"

"I disagree, comrade," interrupted Nobby Hyams. "Shelley was a great revolutionary poet, but not in such rubbish as this. Shelley lived at the time of the industrial revolution. Children were working in the factories for twelve and more hours a day. The workers hardly saw daylight — what was the use of talking to them about "the twilit foam' and "the waves dancing bright'? If he wanted to write a love poem, then he could have written about love in the slums of the new industrial towns —"

"I think you have missed the point, comrade!" said Uncle Jake excitedly.

"Let me finish, comrade!"

"But comrade —!"

"Comrade —!"

"Ssh —!"

The class hushed Uncle Jake into silence, Nobby Hyams finished what he had to say, moved an impromptu resolution which was unanimously carried, Uncle Jake alone abstaining, and the following week Uncle Jake was expelled.

6

AVID FOUND the I.L.P. and the anarchists different from Uncle Jake's first three political parties. The I.L.P. and the anarchists seemed to be defeatist about causes he could not quite ascertain. The members were mostly old and met, he felt, really, only in order to confirm each other's pessimistic prognostications.

"There'll be war in five years —"

"Less, three."

"— or three. The standard of living'll fall —"

"There won't be any standard of living!"

"— well, shall we say the level of subsistence. The ruling class will destroy the workers in their thousands —"

"Millions! There are always plenty of others..."

There was little more to be said.

Uncle Jake's heart was no longer in politics, or even in his studies. He attended meetings once a week, sat in the corner, and spoke little; just as he attended unenthusiastically the final lectures of his degree course and continued to cover mile upon mile of North London streets from pupil to pupil and from library to library. But:

"Too long a sacrifice can make a stone of the heart."

He was no poorer, he was perhaps even a shade better off than fifteen years before. Shortly he would have a degree and might get a congenial job. But his poverty was now more permanent and deeply ingrained, and he was older.

He only just obtained his degree, because during the last couple of years of his degree course, and for a further few years after that, his main interest was the novel which he was writing: *Failure*. The drafting, writing, re-writing, typing, re-typing, submitting, putting aside, re-submitting, acceptance, further rejection, re-acceptance, setting up in type, and final piecemeal publication and distribution of *Failure* was, like the battle for his degree, a heartbreaking business undertaken in hopelessly unfavourable conditions. Getting the novel typed by friends, since there was no question of his being able to pay a professional typist, alone took nearly a year for the first version and a year and a half for the second. Getting the single battered manuscript back from publishers — "blackguards, rogues, thieves, tricksters, swine, dogs, morons, and vermin," fulminated the usually mild-tongued Jake against those who remained benignly indifferent to his impatience — this took several months on each occasion. And finally the agreement: £30 down and a remote possibility of royalties; and the sale: three hundred copies; and the absence of reviews, except in the *North London Gazette,* the *Jewish Magazine,* the *Madras Daily Courier,* and the *Saskatchewan Free Press* — *Failure.*

But long before this the war had come. Uncle Jake was a Sergeant-Instructor in the educational branch of the R.A.F. Later he was commissioned as an Education Officer. He taught illiterates how to read and write, conducted quizzes, discussions, and general-knowledge tests. At the end of the war he signed on as a regular for a further seven years. The surviving elders of the synagogue who remembered him as a boy, were confirmed in their opinions when they heard this piece of news: "Mad! Plainly mad! Everyone else is signing off, and he's signing on!"

But Uncle Jake was in his forties and he welcomed the security and comfortable monotony of his life in the R.A.F.: also, in an odd way, he may have relished the irony of it, the piquant bitterness of his gesture, the negation of his youth. Above all, he wanted to return to London as rarely as possible, and never to the districts and people he had known. He had married, too, a Scots girl whom he had met during the war, and very soon he was the father of two children: the R.A.F. offered living quarters for his family in the large camp where he served, and this was important during the post-war housing shortage.

As for politics, writing, philosophical discussion, he could not be bothered with them at all. He disliked mention of his novel. "Oh, *that!*" he said shortly, and immediately talked of something else. His favourite activity, apart from playing with his children, was gardening.

He lost touch completely with the family. David sought him out once or twice, but though Jake was entirely friendly and hospitable, there was an atmosphere of constraint between them and their relationship was quietly wrapped up, as it were, placed in the cupboard of limbo, and locked away.

Jake's reticence was such that David did not know until years later that *Failure* had in fact been published. He discovered its existence by looking up Jake's name — for fun, really, since he hardly expected after all those years and in the face of Jake's own recent indifference, to find that the novel had at last, been published — in the catalogue of the British Museum. Yes, Jake's name was there, with *Failure* (A Novel) as the single entry beside it.

With what strange feelings David opened the thin, ill-printed, yellow-wrappered volume. It was as though the past itself had been drawn, temporarily but without noticeable change, from the vaults of the museum: that most mysterious and disturbing, remote and inaccessible of epochs, the immediate past, of which Thomas Mann had written:

"Is not the pastness of the past the profounder, the completer, the more legendary, the more immediately before the present it falls?"

And the book itself? David could not attempt to judge its value for others. Its style and technique were adequate, without easily discernable faults or virtues. Its theme was logically developed and completed: *Failure*.

But around its simple and unexceptionable framework, there arose before David, in the pages of the unsuccessful and unread novel, a period and an environment: the streets of North London in the nineteen-thirties, the

127

labour exchanges, the public libraries, the parks, the bed-sitting-rooms, rain on the pavements, fog over the railway yards, and Uncle Jake in an old mackintosh cycling immortally, eternally, towards dreams more real than the reality in which they had been forgotten.

PART SIX
TONY

1

TONY SAVOURED words and phrases, anecdotes and fabulous lies, as he savoured the food which he wolfed with such a show of pleasure, such smacking of lips, gurgling of juices, and ecstatic eye-rolling, in his mother's kitchen and the room behind his uncle's delicatessen shop. He enjoyed them, and, still more, he wanted to be seen enjoying them; he wanted there to be no doubt that he was revelling, simply wallowing, in words as in cakes, in extraordinary tales as in fried fish with pickles. Tony had the innocuous but quite determined ambition to be seen enjoying life with more zest, vim, force, go and laughter than had ever yet been shown by a member of the sluggish human species.

He lit up everything with his sense of wonder, with the sparkling and spluttering incandescence of his imagination. No words were spoken casually; even a remark about the weather became a superlative on Tony's lips, the vowels hissed with concentrated force, the consonants hammered down with shattering vigour.

"This is *the most* cloudy day since last winter!"

David and Tony found themselves going home from school together and Tony very soon fixed David's role in his mythos. David was the commentator, the dreamer, the man of high, impractical vision; of remote intellect, imagination, and quixotic sentiment; at the same time not without a vein of curious cunning, bravado, and mendaciousness. Tony summed it up with the parting words, accompanied by a furious and slightly condescending thump on the back:

"Good old David!"

In contrast, he, Tony, was a person of tremendous and ruthless practical capacity, one who trampled others underfoot if necessary — though fortunately, favoured as he was by the gods, he did not have to — in order to get just what he wanted. He demonstrated his irresistible methods with girls.

"Just come with me into this phone-box," he said, "and you'll hear *the most* amusing conversation you have *ever* heard in your *whole life*!"

They squeezed into a box and Tony dialled a number in Stamford Hill.

"Hullo," he said, and nudged David ecstatically — the fun had already started. "Can I speak to Phyllis, please?"

There was a slight hitch, as Phyllis was not in and her mother wanted to know if there was any message.

"No, no message. Just say that Tony phoned," he added meaningfully, digging David in the ribs.

He maintained the interest of the situation at fever pitch while he dialled another number.

"Hullo."

"Hullo."

"Can I speak to Sylvia, please?"

"Just a moment."

He nudged and dug at David again so that his friend should not miss a word of what followed.

A girl's voice sounded at the other end of the line.

"Hullo!"

"Hullo."

When the girl spoke, Tony held the receiver out in the middle of the phonebox so that David should be able to hear.

"Who's speaking?"

Tony raised his eyebrows at David. He was calmer now and displayed a masterly confidence. You see, he indicated, you see what's happening?

"This is Tony."

He held the receiver out as though it were going to explode at this stupendous statement.

"What?"

"Tony."

"Oh, hullo."

"Hullo."

The first act was over. David waited expectantly for the second. Tony crouched over the phone confidentially, holding the receiver at an angle to his ear, half including David — audience and friend — half excluding him — intruder.

"How are you?"

"Not too bad. How are you?"

"So-so, you know. Bearing up." Wicked chuckle.

"What you been doing?"

"Oh, the usual things, you know. Ha-ha-ha! What about you?"

"Nothing special."

Pause.

"I wonder."

"What do you mean — you wonder?"

"Ha-ha-ha!"

"Don't be silly."

Tony waved at David, as though to say: this is opening your eyes a bit, ay?

Third and final act.

"Well, I'll be pushing along now."

"Yeh. Thanks for ringing."

"It was a pleasure." Meaningful chuckle.

"Yeh. Seen Ted lately?"

"Not since last Saturday. Well, I'll be pushing along now. Might be round your way Sunday."

"Yeh. Ted's giving a party. His mother and father are gonna be out, they're going to a wedding."

"Well, so-long."

"So-long."

"So-lo-ong!"

Tony replaced the receiver with a smirk of satisfaction, a faraway look in his eyes.

"Good old David!" he said, banging his friend violently on the back. "Let's go and have some tea at my place. My mother's left some of *the most* delicious cake you have *ever* seen in your whole life."

They went round to his place to discuss everything. Tony lived in Meresham Road — *"the most* gloomy road in *all* Hackney" — and they stood in the bay-window of his house watching the buses pass and staring out towards the goods yards, railway-lines, and factories of South Hackney. Every now and again Tony darted off to fetch a piece of cake or to show David something — "Look at this chest-expander. Watch the way I stretch it: did you ever see neck-muscles like mine?"

Then he prowled around restlessly and snatched up a medical text-book.

"Medicine! Why don't you take up medicine? Or law? Think of the money in it! Sir Stafford Cripps gets £20,000 for a single case. You could do that. You're as good as Sir Stafford Cripps, aren't you?" he asked earnestly. He swivelled his head round in front of David's and peered up into his friend's face at close quarters, as though the answer were to be found there.

"You know," he said, "you've got some pimples on your forehead. I know!" he anticipated, "mine are worse. I'll show you what to do about it." He hurried off to the kitchen, urging David to follow quickly. There was no time to waste. They both held their faces over steaming basins to get rid of blackheads.

"That's better!" exclaimed Tony when they had finished and were able to examine their lobster-coloured skins in the mirror. Tony patted, adjusted, and fingered the waves in his hair, smirked at himself in the kitchen mirror, darted into the front-room to smirk in the mirror there, ran upstairs to make use of the bedroom mirrors, and then came back to the kitchen, singing all the while in his pleasant falsetto invented

132

snatches from opera in his own operatic, Italian-like language.

"Caro por mio chaveccia d'amor
O por amore mi carito amor
Luccia! Luccia! caro d'amor!..."

2

TONY MADE David aware of the local fascist movement. David knew that two or three anti-semitic parties whose members wore black, blue, or grey shirts had recently been formed, but he had not yet seen anything of them. Coming home from school one day, he and Tony saw walking in front of them two of their schoolfellows, a pair of long, thin boys named Steen and Dunnard. Steen was a snivelling, weak type who did not matter, but Dunnard was a formidable person who aspired, in appearance and manner, towards being what would later have been called a "spiv". He looked about five years older than his true age of fifteen, and the moment he got clear of the school gates lit a cigarette. His hair was worn long and then cut in an abrupt line above his smoothly-shaven neck. His rather cheap suit had squarely padded shoulders and billowing trousers. Every now and again he took out a knife and flung it at any piece of wood in sight, where it came quiveringly to rest. All the while he chewed gum.

"You see those two geezers," said Tony, who in spite of his youth had just been made a prefect, "they're blackshirts. The other day I said to Dunnard, 'Put your school cap on and take that cigarette out of your mouth', and d'you know what he had the nerve to say to me? 'I'll slit you from ear to ear!' So I had him up before the old man and he's in detention for next week. And boy, would he like to do me!"

It was true, for as they passed the two louts, Dunnard said to Steen in a loud voice: "Someone's gonna get done one of these days."

The fascist movement and political violence generally now exercised a morbid fascination over Tony and eventually over David. Not that they ever dreamt of taking active part in the street-corner scrimmages which soon became commonplace at certain open-air pitches. Nor were they there as disinterested spectators. They were there partly out of curiosity, partly drawn by fear, amazement, and indignation, and partly also for the sheer vulgar horror of the thing.

The northern end of Kenliffe Road, between tall, ugly houses on one side and a large, empty churchyard on the other, was a favourite pitch for the first fascist meetings. They would begin quietly and end with mass chants and demonstrations held back by mounted police, the whole lit by the dim, grey-blue lighting of Stoke Newington Road. A contingent arrived shouting:

"The Yids! The Yids! We gotta get rid-a the Yids!" The police viewed this with a stolid and tolerant eye. But the counter demonstration was hedged in by mounted constabulary: "One, two, three-four-five, we want Ozzy dead or alive!" — Ozzy being, of course, Mosley, the new "Leader", though at first his movement was only one of several. Often, among the blackshirts, David and Tony spotted Steen and Dunnard. If the latter saw them, too, Dunnard would make a throat-slitting gesture, which enraged Tony to the point of saying: "I'll *kill* him! I'll really *kill* him!" Only David's restraining hand prevented Tony from doing so there and then, man of passion that he was, of terrible vengeance and incalculable strength.

But there were two sixth-formers at school who actually did take part in the battles with the fascists, and David and Tony consoled themselves by listening to the monosyllabic accounts of the older boys' exploits. They

were East-Enders named Borodik and Kraganitz, who
had come to the school after matriculation to prepare for
the first medical examination in the science department.
Their appearance was reassuringly tough. Borodik was
broad and stocky, with a jutting chin and flattened nose.
Kraganitz loomed over him, with a bulging forehead, long
arms with huge fists at the end of them, and a flattened
nose too. Together, the one looming from above, the other
planted foursquare below, they were complementary and
formidable. They did not bother with the school fascists,
mere boys whose threats were empty, but joined real and
courageous battles at various meetings and riots with the
blackshirts and the police who defended them. After reading in the newspapers of some frightful set-to in Bethnal
Green, David and Tony would inspect Borodik and
Kraganitz, and sure enough Borodik had plaster over his
eye and Kraganitz a bandaged fist.

"What happened?" asked Tony.

"A potato —" said Borodik.

"Yeh?"

"With razor-blades stuck in it."

"A cop bashed me," said Kraganitz.

"But we'll get "em," said Borodik.

"We'll get "em so's they won't show their faces in the
East End no more."

The last time David and Tony saw them was a year or
two after Borodik and Kraganitz had left school. Their
faces covered with blood, they each grimly and silently
struggled with three policemen, who pushed and carried
them into a waiting van. The occasion was the "Battle of
Whitechapel", when some thousands of police fought with
many tens of thousands of demonstrators in an attempt
to clear a way for Sir Oswald Mosley at the head of a pro-
cession of blackshirts to march down Whitechapel High
Street. Tony and David had arrived early in the forefront
of the demonstrators, but very soon took refuge from the
heavings and swaying of the crowd in a block of offices in
Aldgate, where they watched the day's events from a

second-floor window. All but the most determined of the crowd had been driven from this part of the street, which was under the control of the police. Almost the last to be arrested were Borodik and Kraganitz, and when he saw their brave, ineffectual struggle, Tony gripped David's arm and squeezed it.

"God!" he said. "Those boys! They're the real thing!"

"Yeh," said David. "They're the right stuff all right."

3

THEIR FAVOURITE place for talking was in the bay of Tony's front window looking out on Meresham Road. The road David lived in was too quiet to provide much interest; whereas Meresham Road, although "*the* most gloomy road in *all* Hackney", connected Homerton and Dibley with Mare Street and the Public Library, and everyone passed down it sooner or later.

Tony savoured people as he savoured anecdotes and food. He smacked his lips over them; they were the most interesting people imaginable, whether they were schoolmates or acquaintances from the barber's shop round the corner, whose boastings were so stupendous that they left even Tony silent. They sloped along Meresham Road, unaware that they were being observed, until Tony, having nudged David ecstatically — "here's a geezer for you!" — dashed out to the front gate and urged them to come in.

In the summer holidays after David and Tony had matriculated, they were standing in the bay-window watching the evening sun sink behind the railway yards. They were bored and uneasy; even the courage of adolescence failed before the spectacle of summer sunshine in Meresham Road. It would be unbearable, they felt, to spend August in such ignoble, such hopeless, such finally depressing surroundings after a paltry ten days at Southend and Brighton respectively. Tony prowled restlessly from the bookcase to the window, now opening a book on forensic medicine to show David the mutilated corpse of some famous murder case — he had already, before beginning his preliminary course, collected a library of unusual medical text-books and was known in the barber's shop as the "Doc"... now pausing to finger and adjust the waves in his hair, now banging David absent-mindedly on the back and saying — "Why don't you enter the diplomatic service? Or why don't you write a best-seller...? *Do* something with your life! Don't let it slip away!"

Then he saw Greenbaum, the tall, sad Greenbaum, not his small, melancholy brother, walking along, bowed with grief, on the other side of the road. Tony dug David furiously in the ribs.

"Grinny," he said, "I'll fetch him in. That geezer'll be the death of me one of these days."

David watched Grinny follow Tony meekly into the house. Tony, small, compact, dynamic, bubbled ahead, rubbing his hands, grinning, fingering his hair to make sure it was all still there and in the right place, and with the air of a cheerful and energetic surgeon leading a patient to the operating table. He plumped Grinny in a chair, said "Well?", creased all his features into an enormous preparatory laugh, and before even the sad-faced Greenbaum had soberly, reflectively, and with dignity begun to open his mouth — "This geezer has me worried," said Tony to David. "I feel I ought to *do* something for him. Cheer up, Grinny!"

"That is most unnecessary," said Greenbaum, "though I appreciate your solicitude, because I am as a matter of fact highly cheered up. I have just returned from a hitch-hiking expedition to Kent, and tomorrow I am setting out on another to Surrey. It is you I commiserate with for being stuck, during this admirable weather, in these gloomy surroundings."

The idea hit Tony instantly: they would all go hitch-hiking together. So the next day, each with about ten shillings in his pocket, they took the tram to South London, got a lift from a lorry-driver to within a few miles of Guildford, sunbathed, ate all their stocks of sandwiches, and considered their plans for the night. Ten shillings was not a lot of money, and they wanted to stay "on-the-road" for at least a week. They had some idea of doing odd jobs at houses and farms, such as chopping wood — always a good standby in hitchhiking-planning — or digging gardens.

They struck off the main road without any definite objective, Tony all the while teasing the life out of Grinny, who was gravely, philosophically, and loudly drawing in great lungfuls of country air and letting them out in bursts — "Aaah! Aaah! Make the most of the country while you can." David was hot and tired and very much attracted by the smooth, shady lawns of a large house on the side of a hill.

"Let's go and ask for some water," said David. "Then somebody may come out, ask us to tea, and invite us to stay the night. By doing that we shall get along without spending any money at all."

"A singularly infantile notion," said Greenbaum.

However, David was not far out in his wishful fancy. A pleasant, elderly lady, flanked by four large, amiable dogs came to the door. She asked them what they were. They said that they were students. Tony added that *he* was a medical student, that David was a student of the Arts, and that Greenbaum was a "theorist".

"A theorist?" said the lady reflectively. The dogs looked up at her inquiringly. "Won't you come in?" she said eventually, and led them through the house on to the lawn. "I'll have the maid prepare you some tea — I suppose you could do with some tea?" They made polite, but hungry noises of nominal disagreement and real assent.

Lying on the smooth, shady lawn, with the variegated

sylvan patchwork of the Surrey countryside spread out before them, sipping tea from china tea-cups and fussed around by the four large, amiable dogs, they felt that hitchhiking was very worthwhile.

On the road again, they broke themselves sticks from branches, sang songs in French and in Tony's Italianate operatic language, cut across fields and followed quiet lanes till they found themselves, when it was growing dark, at a very rustic-looking village named Tarrocksleigh, where for two shillings each they shared a large bed for the night.

On the following day, they moved around in what turned out to be a wide circle, calling at the back doors of country houses and asking for water. Sometimes they got only water, usually lemonade and biscuits, occasionally a snack. David threw out the bright ideas, Tony was very easily discouraged, and Greenbaum provided the grit and tenacity. In the evening they arrived at Brunston Green and found a cricket match in preparation on the village green. As it happened, the cricket teams were several men short and they were approached by one of the captains and invited to play.

Late in the evening, when it was almost dark, David was put on to bowl. Everyone on their side was thoroughly fed up with the batsman who faced David. This batsman had gone in first, stayed in throughout the other team's innings, and scored seven. It was really too dark to play, but they were determined to get the stonewaller out before the game was over. David was a very fast bowler, very fast indeed. No one knew this when he was put on to bowl. He withdrew about thirty yards, began to run, gathered speed, and arrived at the wicket, in the dusk, like a vague flash. His arm whizzed over and the ball disappeared. No one saw it. It was impossible to say where it had gone. The game would perforce have had to stop, if a small boy had not come running up with the ball, saying he had found it outside the Brunston Arms. David took another run, this time of about forty yards. Once again the ball disappeared, without anyone having the least idea where it had gone, and at the same time all three stumps of the opposite wicket flew apart. A brief cheer went up. The teams dispersed quickly and with relief into the darkness, and the captain of their side stood Greenbaum, Tony, and David a round of bread, cheese, and beer at the Brunston Arms: another meal earned.

They shared a bed for the night in a cottage which let rooms — very unwisely, they decided, because the walls were so thin that every embarrassing detail of every bedroom was audible throughout the house. However, they were charged only one and sixpence each. Nevertheless, they began their third day with only twelve shillings between them. Something had to be done if they were to last out a week.

Once again David put forward the bright ideas, but Greenbaum instead of supplying the grit and tenacity, decided to return to London to get out a new library book, having in two days and nights finished *The Dialectic of the Social Revolution.*

"In any case," he said, "the weather's bound to break soon. We've spent our money and we've had our fun —"

"Fun!" exclaimed Tony. "The geezer's read nine hundred pages in two days and he calls that fun! Why don't you take up law? You'd make a marvellous judge, especially for giving the death sentence!"

Tony chuckled and was so pleased with his own joke that he put up no resistance against David's plan. Greenbaum smiled sadly, and near Dorking thumbed a lift from a passing lorry back to the Hackney Public Library.

David's plan was simple and adequate. It was that they should buy second-hand, for about two shillings, a pair of hedge-shears; that they should by-pass London, explore new territory, and make for Cambridge, earning their living by shearing garden-hedges. Say, for instance, they needed ten shillings a day. Very well, they knocked at a house whose garden-hedge needed trimming and offered to do the job for half-a-crown. Their offer was willingly

140

accepted, they repeated the process four times, and then, the day's work over, they wandered on. An ideal existence, David thought, while the weather lasted. Maybe they even did an extra hedge or two, saved a few shillings each day, and returned home in triumph, sunburned and full of experience, with their holiday savings jingling in their pockets. The only thing David could not understand was why no one else had thought of the idea; it was so apt.

They managed to find the hedge-shears for two shillings in a sort of old-iron shop, and after a day's energetic hitchhiking they had cleared London, though the chances of the road deposited them at Bedford instead of Cambridge. When they arrived, it was too late to think of shearing hedges and they were down to their last few shillings. They put up for the night in a room above a café. The room had three beds, one each and one to spare. Having paid the night's rent, they issued out on to Bedford, very hungry and with fourpence between them. They spent the fourpence at the fish-and-chip shop, but remained hungry when the chips had been eaten. They hung around the fish-and-chip shop wondering what to do, when a couple of girls came out with a great pile of hot chips between them.

"Give us a chip," said David.

The girls looked a bit startled and then said: "Sure, help yourself."

They took a chip each, and the girls said: "Have another, go on."

They took another, and the girls left, looking backwards several times in mystification and slight alarm, ready to break into a run at the first sign of trouble. But David and Tony now knew what to do and were already tackling the next pair.

"Give us a chip."

They had soon eaten their fill of chips; one generous girl bought them cups of tea and they left for bed. David had to put up with a lot of grumbling from Tony, who seemed to think, once they had eaten, that there was something undignified in their procedure. Begging, he called it....

"Why don't you write a best-seller?" he said. "Then we could be in the South of France enjoying ourselves."

"Aren't we enjoying ourselves now?" David replied.

"Yes, but it's not the same...."

They did not sleep very well that night. There was a great deal of coming and going on the stairs, and outside the sound of lorries pulling up and driving away. In the middle of the night, the door was flung open. They cowered in their beds, wondering what was going to happen next. There was the thud of heavy boots being dropped on the floor, then someone sank on to the third bed, apparently fully clothed, and began almost immediately to snore. The sound continued all night. When at last, bringing its miraculous renewal of hope, the dawn appeared, they swiftly dressed and went off, leaving their companion, who was wearing even his cap, rasping away on the third bed. David was not sorry to leave Bedford; a dismal, pointless town, he thought it, and recalled, as they breathed in the sweet morning air beside the freshly twittering hedges on the Oxford road, that it was in Bedford jail that Bunyan had been imprisoned and had written *Pilgrim's Progress,* which he had never read.

"That's all I need!" snorted Tony. "Here, let's roll ourselves some cigarettes."

They had brought with them a cigarette-rolling machine and two or three small paper bags of tobacco with which they used to experiment in blending themselves unusually flavoured cigarettes. The morning sun was shining, they sat down by the roadside and bent over the rolling machine. A woman passed by on a bicycle and said, "Good morning." They replied cheerfully, and as David glanced up he noticed how broad and flat was the field in front of them, stretching away to several camouflaged buildings, like small hills in the distance. At the same time a plane rose from near one of these mounds; he realised that they were facing an airfield.

Having lit cigarettes, they hailed an open lorry and clambered on to the back among sacks of potatoes. They stood up, holding on to the top of the cab, and felt the wind rush past their heads exhilaratingly. Tony's spirits revived; he sang loudly in his Italianate operatic language:

"Amor de mi, a mi carito!
Carito d'amor besa me mucho!
Besa me carito!
Amore, amor...."

The words were carried away by the wind among the potato fields and here and there disturbed groups of munching, staring cattle.

Suddenly the lorry came to a halt beside a red house bearing the sign: Police, Bedfordshire County Constabulary. A hatless policeman stood in the middle of the roadway. He took no notice of the lorry-driver, but came round to the back.

"Come on, you two!" he said to Tony and David.

They jumped down. The lorry-driver, after a word or two with the policeman, drove off.

"What's up?" David asked the policeman.

"You answer the description of two youths wanted for taking photographs of the airfield."

"Photographs?" said David.

"Come along inside," said the policeman rather more severely. "We had a report through only ten minutes ago about two foreign-looking youths acting suspiciously by the airfield. The R.A.F. police will be here shortly."

David was relieved and fairly pleased when he heard the charge; it would provide material for an excellent anecdote. But Tony was annoyed and disquieted.

"Foreign-looking!" he said. "Am I foreign-looking?"

"I'm afraid you are," said David.

Tony bucked up after a while when David suggested

143

that they had been taken for Italians. Tony liked the exotic touch.

They were not exotic enough, however, for the R.A.F. Investigation Officer who eventually arrived with a roar in a fast sports car. He was frankly disappointed at finding only a couple of schoolboys from Hackney when he had been prepared for two really exotic spies. He glanced, David thought, a little regretfully at the revolver which he carried handily in a holster strapped round his waist. He tried to vent his disappointment on them.

"It's your own fault," he said angrily. "You should take more care."

They agreed to take more care in future when rolling cigarettes near R.A.F. airfields, and the constable's wife made them all tea. The constable himself was not too happy about the hedge-shears, suspecting, apparently, that they were meant to cut off people's heads and not hedges. But having no definite charge to make, he accepted the Turco-Bulgarian cigarette which Tony and David blended for him and let the two suspects go. He and his wife and the R.A.F. officer stood in the middle of the road outside the house and watched them out of sight. The first car they thumbed some minutes later was the fast sports car driven by the R.A.F. officer, who took them grimly all the way to Oxford — "miles out of his road", he complained.

On the outskirts of Oxford they set to work knocking at the doors of houses with unsheared hedges. Most of the householders looked at them incredulously when they offered to do the job for half-a-crown. "No thanks," they said, "don't trouble." Only one man did any business with them at all. "Here's the half-a-crown," he said, "but don't touch the hedge. Just leave it alone."

At the end of the day, during which they had eaten only a few sandwiches and cups of tea, Tony made the unexpected and enticingly sensible suggestion which is eventually made at the end of all adventures, treks, escapades, journeys round the world, one which in this case could be readily put into effect.

"Let's go home," he said towards evening.

"Capitulation," said David.

"And let's throw away those infernal hedge-shears!"

"Revenge."

However, David made no opposition when Tony took the hedge-shears and tried in vain to tear them apart; nor when at last he plunged them savagely into an unkempt hedge and left them there.

The fates, as though to drive the lesson home — the lesson that one must always be prepared for more trouble — made them wait for two hours on the London road before providing them with a lift. Just as it was getting dark, a vast, heavy lorry, travelling at about five miles an hour, trundled by and came to a halt a hundred yards up the road. They raced up to it, hoping it had stopped for them, and stood by the cab while the driver quizzed them.

"Where d'ye wanna go?"

"London."

"London?"

"Yes."

"Ho." Pause. "Why don't you go by train?"

"We're hitchhiking."

"Wotcher doin' this time o' night?"

"We were stuck here."

"Wodjer do for a livin'?"

"We're students."

"Woss tha'?"

"Well, we're sort of studying."

"Woss tha'?"

"You know, for exams and things."

"Ay?"

"Oh, nothing."

"Got any money?"

"No."

"Wanna go to London, ay," he reflected. "All right, I'll take yer. Fer nothing," he said magnanimously. "But

145

you'll 'ave to 'elp me unload this stuff at the end."

They looked at the enormous lorry piled with old bits of machinery, they looked at the night gathering around them, looked at the lorry-driver's stubble-chinned face and at the speedometer whose upper limit was 15 m.p.h., and they agreed.

Lorry-drivers in general, they had found, were exceptionally obliging. There was little advantage to the lorry-drivers in stopping to pick up hitchhikers, but they did so and thereby put themselves at some risk and inconvenience. This one, however, was a villain. Instead of waiting, according to the etiquette of the road, to be offered cigarettes, he said gruffly:

"Got any cigarettes?"

They blended and rolled him one. He looked suspiciously at the rolling machine and little paper bags of tobacco. When the cigarette was completed, he found difficulty in lighting it, because of course their home-made cigarette lacked saltpetre. He stopped the lorry, and while the giant machine rumbled and trembled, he got the now damp and disintegrating cigarette to light. After a few puffs, he flung it disgustedly out of the window.

"This thing's no damn good!"

He pulled a Woodbine out of his pocket, lit it, and drove on without saying another word till the end of the journey.

He was not even going to London, but to Slough. At half-past one in the morning he drove along the bleak, unlit, and half-made roads of an industrial estate, past long, low factory sheds and over private railway lines, and pulled up inside an immense hangar-like structure. A single fierce bluish light shone from the roof.

"O.K., Jack?" boomed a voice echoing and trailing among the dark spaces beyond the blue area of light.

"O.K., Bill!" said the lorry-driver. The vast doors at the end of the hangar rolled towards each other and thundered to. Tony and David were trapped.

"Now," said the lorry-driver briskly, "let's get crackin'.

Better take yer jackets off, I should think."

For two hours the hitchhikers worked at those old bits of machinery. The old bits of machinery were all heavy and mostly shaped in such a way that it was impossible to get hold of them. They appeared to be quite unbreakable and indestructible, but the lorry-driver kept repeating:

"Careful with that stuff, now! Careful!"

When the job was done, the lorry-driver called out into the dark spaces of the hangar to the unseen controller of the doors:

"O.K. Bill!"

"O.K. Jack!"

The vast doors rumbled apart about a foot. Tony and David squeezed through anxiously, afraid of being crushed to death, and found themselves out in the wilderness of half-made roads, low sheds, and private railway lines. On all sides could be heard the baying of savage dogs....

4

AFTER THEY left school, David did not see Tony for several years. When they met again Tony had a car and a villa in the suburbs. With that car, David judged, Tony was as happy as the day is long. Every action connected with it seemed to give him pleasure: opening the door, getting in with one leg in front of the driving-seat and one in the road, slamming the door, starting the engine, accelerating, decelerating — but chiefly slamming the door. David imagined that for Tony slamming the door gave a final and delightful touch to the artistry of his mode of living — that brave, confident moment when he stepped out of the car, hurried to brisk, fairly urgent, and successful appointments, coat-tails sweeping behind him, face radiant with dynamism, and without turning round, forcefully, masterfully, slammed the door!

They drove to dinner in Tony's villa and were chatting in the dining-room. There was a hatch in the wall, so that the maid could push plates and dishes in without being seen. David felt that the hatch spoiled everything. He could accept, and even admire, the villa, the car, the suburban success — but not a room with a hatch in it. On the other side of the hatch was the maid. What did she look like? What sort of person was she? She became for David a mystery, a disturbing presence, the most interesting, because the most inaccessible and unimaginable person in the villa. But she remained hidden away, segregated behind the hatch. Contact between the two rooms was possible only through the hatch: the question was, which room was the cage, the dining-room or the kitchen?

However, Tony had something to say before the other guests arrived, something, apparently, a little difficult to express.

"Look …" he said, " 'er, David …" He grinned shamefacedly.

"Yes?"

"Look… you see … Hm!"

"Yes?"

"Look … you see … I told them all we once hitchhiked to the South of France."

"Well, you did once hitchhike to Paris, didn't you? But that was with Stanley; not with me."

"Yes, that's right. But you see … er … I told them that I just hitchhiked once to the South of France with you. Just once, for an adventure. You won't say anything about that other time, in Surrey and Bedford, will you? And you won't contradict anything in my story? Ay? There's a pal. It's just a little thing, a silly thing, but … you know."

"I know," said David sympathetically, "rely on me."

After dinner David listened to the revised version of their hitchhiking trip.

"... we were fifteen, we made up our minds to have an adventure, to hitchhike to Italy.... Below us lay the Mediterranean .... we waved our coloured handkerchiefs, a huge roadster stopped and carried us on to Nice.... We drank wine on the terrace, and afterwards, at the Casino, we won enough to go on to Venice.... Ah! those days will never return!"

PART SEVEN
THE ALEXANDROVICH
FAMILY

1

"**L**OOK — LOOK — LOOK!**" exclaimed Tony one evening from the bay window of his front room looking out on Meresham Road. "There's Alexey!" He gave his chuckle of pure fun and derision, against which no human vanity could stand upright for long. "Alexey!" he giggled. "Alec Alexandrovich, Joseph Stalin's right-hand man. There's a geezer for you!" He shot out of the house to bring Alexey in for surgical treatment, as it were.

But David knew Alexey better than Tony and fancied he would be unamenable to Tony's light-hearted surgery.

There was a long conversation on the other side of the road, with Tony waving, grinning, and gesticulating towards the house and Alexey staring nonchalantly in the other direction. Finally Tony led the way into the house, looking over his shoulder every few steps to make sure that Alexey was following; and Alexey, glancing everywhere except at Tony and the house, did actually follow in a sort of abstract, disinterested way. He came into the room, turning his head from side to side and flinging it back to redispose the two loose waves of his hair round its centre parting, pouting and shaping his lips to make them seem fuller, running his fingertips along walls, touching furniture, handling knick-knacks, peering at photographs; and, nodding vaguely to David, sank into a chair. Then his eyes came to rest, as though by accident, on Tony, who was grinning just a little uncertainly.

"Well, what day's the revolution?" was all Tony could think of saying.

Alexey smiled in his turn, the unique Alexey smile. Hundreds of hours of practice in front of the mirror had been necessary in order to bring that smile to its full beastliness. David was never, later, able to recall or describe the smile directly, as it appeared from the outside. After the passage of years it still made him feel uneasy. He could think of it only in terms of how the smile was probably conceived in Alexey's mind. Alexey probably described it to himself as a sardonic smile, a cynical smile, a cryptic smile, a strange, disturbing, heartless, cruel smile, mysterious, enigmatic, ironic, unforgettable. He must have formed sentences such as the following to describe the smile in action:

"The arcs of his full, red lips parted symmetrically to display two gleaming rows of even white teeth. Katya momentarily felt a tremor of fear, replaced instantly by a sense of wonder, of hypnotised fascination, of heedless yearning, such as made all her life up to that moment appear drab, commonplace, and savourless."

Or:

"Alexey's soft, negroid lips curved voluptuously over his brilliant teeth, strong, white, and smooth as the man within. Sonia wanted those lips to descend implacably over hers, wanted helplessly to be overborne by the sardonic strength of the man behind that enigmatic, that disturbingly exotic smile."

Alexey, then, smiled. Tony and David stared at his teeth. There was nothing to do when Alexey smiled except examine his teeth and grudgingly admit that they were in splendid condition, even if somewhat too protruding to be really admirable. Then Alexey spoke: his voice was a high-powered whine.

"Shall I tell you what your face reminds me of?" he said to Tony. "A cat's bottom."

Tony grinned shamefacedly. His humorous ethos required that he should laugh at jokes made against himself too, but David felt sorry when this had to happen. Nevertheless David laughed out loud; the comparison was so apt.

Alexey whined at David: "All right, you've got nothing to laugh about." David waited apprehensively. What terrible simile was now going to be loosed on him? Fortunately Alexey preferred to demand food. He may or may not have wanted food, but asking for it as uncouthly as possible he was able to drive his point home, namely that Alexey was an impossible, outrageous person. The corollary was of course that Alexey was a great person, a future Lenin or Stalin or Trotsky, say: were not all great men, argued Alexey, impossible and outrageous, detested by the small fry around them? And was he not universally detested and always in trouble? What further proof could be wanted?

"Give me some cake," he said. "Cheese-cake or currant-cake. I don't want any plain-cake, and I'll have some garlic sausage with it." He unveiled his lips to bare his teeth and gave the announcement the genuine Alexey touch.

"Sure," said Tony, "sure," rubbing his hands and trying to bubble cheerfully and normally. He wanted to display, to chuckle, to slice up, and to display again, a demonstrating surgeon of laughter. But Alexey could not be sliced, could not even be snicked. He was made, less of steel, than of tough, infinitely twistable, shapeless, and apparently quite unimpressionable rubber. He gobbled his cake and sausage as loudly and greedily as possible and left, whining:

"I've got more important things to do than sit here listening to your drivel."

Once he had gone, Tony came up to David, peered right into his face, and grinned widely; quite sincerely, too, because he had found the anecdotal formula for Alexey.

"Well, wha'd' I tell you? The biggest rat in all Hackney!

152

The trouble is, he's got a head on his shoulders as well. He's got the brain of a man of fifty. You can't put anything past him. He'll do something big one day. God knows what it'll be … probably blow up the Town Hall or something. But what a rat, ay! What a geezer!"

2

THE Alexandroviches were, in every sense except that of absolute fact, Russian. They were a family out of, say, Dostoievsky: atheist father, simple-minded mother, diabolist son, beautiful daughter, all living by candle-light in two rooms piled with old encyclopaedias and backless nineteenth-century text-books and littered with atheist tracts, the broken windows stuffed with sacking, the flat-door barred against intruders. The family life of the Alexandrovich family within those two rooms at the top of a large, gloomy, and dilapidated house near Victoria Park, had never actually been witnessed by an outsider. David could only visualise scenes from books with titles (sometimes quite misleading) like *Dead Souls, The Golovlyov Family, The House of the Dead, What Shall We Do?*

The Alexandrovich family was ethnically no more and no less Slavonic than other Jewish families in Hackney and Dibley who had been resident for one, two, or three generations in England. The Alexandroviches were not even among the most recent arrivals from Eastern Europe: old man Alexandrovich had been loafing around the Hackney Public Library for the best part of half a century. Nevertheless, the Alexandroviches liked to give themselves a Russian air. They adopted Russian names. Alec became Alexey, Netty became Natasha, and the parents were Alexandrov and Alexandrova.

Then they dressed in a sort of Russian fashion. Alexey

had an extra long overcoat — "a Rrohssian overcoat". He always dramatically and profoundly pronounced Russia as "Rrohssia"; it sounded more Russian. He sometimes wore a cap like a bus conductor's cap — "a Rrohssian cap" — and long rubber boots — "Rrohssian boots". Alexandrov wore his coat long, too, and had his hat pushed out of shape in a way that was somehow "Rrohssian".

The beautiful Natasha appeared at her most distinguished in a high, black cossack hat; while Alexandrova's shapeless mass, padded with layer after layer of old dresses, skirts, pinafores, and shawls, her vacuous, uncomplaining smile, and incessant low mumbling, were recognisably Dostoievskian.

As likely as not, anywhere within earshot of Alexey or Alexandrov one caught the words — "In Russia ... In Moscow... The Russians ... Stalin ... Trotsky ..." Trotsky was linked with Russia as Alexandrov's main theme: how he had met Trotsky in 1907, how Trotsky had acknowledged his letter in 1922, how Trotsky had been right and the others wrong; how even Trotsky had sometimes been wrong and Alexandrov had been right. Alexey insisted on the same themes, except that he thought his father a fool — "a silly, stupid, lazy, good-for-nothing old idiot".

"The biggest mistake in Trotsky's life," he said, "was to speak to my father in 1907."

Alexandrov was always to be seen in and near the Public Library. It was not possible to be within three hundred yards of the Public Library without seeing Alexandrov. He might say that he was going between two places that had no connection with the Public Library; nevertheless, a quite fortuitous meeting with Alexandrov was sure to take place within sight of the library steps. Or David might be travelling down Mare Street late at night on a bus, long after the library had closed; without a doubt, glancing out of the window, he would see — by chance — Alexandrov walking towards some definite objective along the pavement near the Public Library.

On Thursday evenings the neighbourhood of the Public Library seemed to be full of Alexandrovs. He was in the lending department, the reading-room, on the steps, and arguing at the street-corner meeting on the other side of the road all at the same time. "In Russia ... The Russians ... Stalin ... Trotsky ... atheism ..." He did no work and the family lived on the money his wife earned as a char. "I've worn myself out by a lifetime of work," he said to the street corner speakers, "and what have I got to show for it? Trotsky said to me in 1907 ..."

3

IN SPITE of being an atheist, Alexandrov sent his son, for some reason, to the Dibley Talmud Torah Hebrew Classes, where Alexey, at a very early age, organised an atheist group. There were unusual arguments which concluded with Alexey's expulsion. Visiting rabbis came to test the boys on the term's work.

"Why must a Jew not carry a handkerchief on the Sabbath day?" was the question put to Alexey.

"So that he can get used to emptying his nose with his thumb and forefinger," replied Alexey.

"What? What does the boy say?" asked the rabbi, whose English was not too good.

"Nothing, nothing, a bad boy," said the headmaster hastily, lightly dusting his trouser-leg with the cane he carried around with him as a sort of walking-stick.

"But it was an interesting answer, perhaps? What did the boy say?"

"He's an epicurean."

"An epicurean? God forbid! At such an early age!" The rabbi raised his hand imploringly heavenwards. "He'll grow out of it...."

Alexey was caned for his beliefs; but instead of leaving the Hebrew classes he persuaded his father to bring a court action for assault. The action was finally settled out of court by Alexandrov agreeing to withdraw his son from the classes on receiving 27s. 6d. as damages.

For several years David saw Alexey only occasionally in the street or at the Public Library, where, should a room be for a few moments undisturbed by Alexandrov's insistent polemics, Alexey's high, drawling whine would probably be heard. David spoke to him at first with a certain feeling of guilt, because within the Hirsch family circle Alexey was referred to as "the Madman".

"What do you want to go speaking to the Madman for?"

Alexey did not ease the difficulties of their acquaintanceship by invariably greeting David with:

"Hullo, you fool!"

and going away with:

"I've got more important things to do than stand here listening to your drivel."

However, every now and again they spoke. Alexey did not mind much either way. Speaking to Alexey, David found, was like setting the needle on a gramophone record or putting a coin in a juke-box. The interlocutor said something, the record at once started playing, and went on without the possibility of interruption to the end. If the gramophone needed winding, or if, unable to stand the record for a second longer, the interlocutor took Alexey by the throat and attempted to strangle him, Alexey, simply strolled off nonchalantly, making the following noise with his lips: "Bub."

But this was not to say that Alexey's conversation was uninteresting or monotonous. If it had been, no one would have put up with him; whereas in fact David was merely one of a large number of people who went out of their way, in the face of insults and jeers, to seek out Alexey's opinions.

"What do you think of so-and-so, Alexey?"

"So-and-so ..." steadily to the end of the record.

Though speaking to Alexey was like setting a needle to a gramophone record, there was a great variety of records. Choice of subject was quite free and depended solely on the first seizable word used.

"Why do you think Mr. Baldwin —?"

Or just:

"Mr. Baldwin —"

There was no question of Alexey's letting the interlocutor go any further than that. As soon as the syllable "Bald —" had been pronounced, with a whirr and a whine the record was on:

"Mr. Baldwin ..."

steadily to the end. And then: "I'm going now. I've got more important things to do than listen to your drivel." But the records were from time to time revised and brought up-to-date. They were, in their own odd, tendentious way, well-informed and provocative.

4

THEY MET at various times, "the Madman" and David, mainly in the street; then Alexey turned up at David's new school, Stenholme College. There he sat, unexpectedly and yet, somehow, inevitably, with his cool, brazen, yet inwardly shamefaced, lonely defiance, his jaw working up and down in a steady, nutcracker-like movement as he held forth to the usual jeering crowd.

There were people, David later thought, whom one did not know very well, with whom one had, nevertheless, a sort of mystical relationship, in which existed an awareness of a curious parallelism of destiny. About such people, without inquiring, one knew everything; and vice versa. Of course this parallelism might have lain very deep — the relationship was mystical — and in fact the two participants might have appeared quite dissimilar, lived quite dissimilarly, and met only rarely. But each knew that the other would turn up, somehow, somewhere, with a fateful irony. That was how he had felt when he saw Alexey sitting in the desk next to his own at Stenholme College some two years after he, David, had entered the school and left Alexey behind, so he had thought, at Dibley Road.

At Stenholme College, as formerly at Dibley Road, Alexey became a school character, always in trouble. He would have been in far greater trouble had allowance not been made for him as a character. Wearily masters and prefects exclaimed:

"It's Alexandrovich again!"

And resignedly:

"Oh, it's only Alexandrovich!"

Alexey broke nearly all the school rules in existence at that time, and several more the necessity for which nobody had previously foreseen. Who but Alexey would have thought of spreading out a dozen differently-coloured bottles of ink on his desk and writing each line — sometimes, for distinction, each word — in a different colour? Who but Alexey would have persistently interrupted the history lesson with cries of: "Non-marxist and unscientific!"? Or reported the gym-instructor to the police for threatening language? Or tried to convert the whole of the Masters' Common Room to communism?

In the end it was decided to leave him alone. "Leave Alexandrovich alone!" There was nothing to be done with him. Every now and again he ran away, but always turned up again. The police paid his fare home or he was repatriated by the British consul. On the following Monday morning he appeared at school again, a little chastened, but quietly proud.

"Alexandrovich is back from Paris. The British consul bought his ticket home."

158

"The police picked him up in Soho. He said he'd lost his memory."

In the year before matriculation David did very badly indeed. He was sent into the lowest class preparing for the examination and into the "hopeless" class for mathematics. That mathematics class filled him with private shame — private, because it was held in a classroom on its own at the far end of the school and David scarcely knew the other rejects among whom he was consigned. After morning service, his friends bustled off brightly and vigorously and full of hopeful purpose to their mathematics classes, the classes of those who had a chance of passing the examination. Discreetly they said nothing about where David was going: and David slunk off alone to Class E at the far end of the school. At first he gave way to despair and wrote poetry throughout the maths lesson, dark poetry of bitter resignation or poetry of escape. The maths master was holding out against numerous ailments and afflictions until the date for his retirement fell due at the end of the year; he spent a good part of the lesson with his head buried in a handkerchief under the desk, pretending to be doing something in the bottom drawer, but actually coughing, sniffing, inhaling from bottles, and sampling pills. For all that, he remained a good teacher. He exercised no pressure and progress depended entirely on the pupil's will to work. During the first term David had no will to work and slid towards the tail-end even of Class E. Meanwhile he filled exercise book after exercise book with verse.

On the first day of the second term, having arrived from Paris or the Great North Road or merely from some other class — David could not be sure — Alexey, mystical co-traveller whose destiny crossed his own at odd, incalculable points, sat in the desk behind David's, writing verse in green ink. David tried to carry on as usual with his verse-writing when Alexey, leaning over from the desk behind, tapped him on the shoulder.

"Plagiarist!" hissed Alexey.

159

"How can I be plagiarising from you when you're sitting in the desk behind?"

"I've got more important things to do than listen to your drivel."

"Why, you —!"

"Shut up!" said Alexey loudly, so that everyone, including the maths master, should look up and see that he was not responsible for the disturbance which he had himself caused.

"Now, now," mumbled the maths master.

David decided to stop writing poetry and instead to work seriously at maths, which he very soon decided was an unjustly maligned subject. He found solving riders and algebraic problems at least as interesting a pastime as building up sonnets. He became almost a toady to the maths master, drawing him into continual private conferences at the master's desk and asking him to explain points which he had already gone over ad nauseam with the rest of the class. And at the same time David became something of a bore to his friends in the matriculation year by continually trying to interest them in cute little riders and algebraic trick problems. To begin with, these problems were so elementary that everyone laughed, knowing that David was near the bottom of Class E. Afterwards they were questions which were not likely to be set in the examination. The whole thing was taken to be a pretentious cover for David's commonplace backwardness in maths and most other subjects. But in fact David's new enthusiasm for maths spread within him until it covered the other subjects and penetrated into every corner of the syllabus. For six months, every evening until after midnight and all through the weekends, he worked with enthusiasm, application, and unanticipated pleasure.

Sometimes he noticed that after a group in the playground had rapidly broken up on seeing him approach with yet another problem, Alexey remained, and quite humbly and patiently waited to see what it was all about;

160

and days later, long after David had solved it or given it up, Alexey was still worrying away at it and pestering the clever boys in the matriculation year to consider this "very interesting problem, most unusual", which they had learned long ago or did not need to know. And once or twice David caught Alexey studying class text-books with some concentration, though Alexey denied, of course, that he was working for matriculation like any ordinary schoolboy.

Destiny: strange, capricious drama…. Eighty boys of Stenholme College were assembled in the hall to hear the matriculation results. Theodore, "the genius", with a distinction in every subject, headed the list of those who had passed. There was a brief laugh of applause; no one had expected anything less of Theodore. Two clever and hard-working boys came second with five distinctions each: no surprise there. David came next with four distinctions. There was a whistle of astonishment; heads were turned in his direction.

"Luck," murmured some.

"Cribbing," said others.

Then the headmaster himself, white-haired Repston Fermoy, sought to create an effect. He stepped back with a grin, held up the list, and said loudly, in his impressive bark that was almost a yelp: "Fifth, Alexey Alexandrovich, with three distinctions." Groans, boos, ironic cheers, and cries of incredulity dissolved gradually into laughter, the stamping of feet, and a rhythmic clapping.

"Enough!" The headmaster held up his hand; the fun and sensation were over. The grim and fateful recital of names continued — "who shall live and who shall die, who by fire and who by sword, who by famine and who by pestilence". In the hearts of those who heard after their names the syllables "— 'triculation, there was leaping and dancing, as though they had escaped from bondage for ever, into a world of freedom and light, of beauty and pleasure.

5

AFTER matriculating, Alexey left Dibley. For a while he may, late at night, have crept back to sleep in his parents' two rooms and have hurried quickly away in the morning — David did not know, he never saw him, and Alexey's voice no longer set people's nerves on edge in the reading-room of the Public Library: to all intents and purposes Alexey had left the district. His sister, the beautiful Natasha, had gone before him. She had never, in any case, belonged to Dibley. She had no friends there, spoke to no one, and was in fact only to be seen on her way to and from the bus stop and slipping, with a sudden turn and a swift glide, up the steps of her house into — who knew what, behind the dust-encrusted, broken windows stuffed with sacking?

Natasha left Hackney while still in her early 'teens; and David felt that her early departure was both inevitable and right. Not that he had ever spoken to her; that would not have been proper. For in the formal hierarchy of his childhood imaginings Natasha was undisputedly a princess — "the distant princess". Tall and slim, swift and silent, wearing her black Cossack cap, she slipped through the rough streets of Dibley with such grace and beauty and speed that not even the tongues of the gossips had time and opportunity to start wagging and clacking.

In odd parts of London and at odd times David saw Alexey. Very rarely they came face to face and Alexey would slightly raise one eyebrow — a difficult movement which had required much practice — coolly and incuriously, and say, "Oh, hullo." There was the merest suggestion that David had been following him. In Hampstead, for instance, David, in the company of Stanley, once helped to roneo the sheets of *Poetry and the New Era;* when a girl with hair hanging over one eye said, "That *awful* man ..." sure enough, Alexey came into the room. At Marble Arch, a group of disputants were hooting somebody at their centre; David heard a familiar high-powered whine — Alexey. On a tube-escalator a woman's voice burst out: "For Christ's sake, shut up! And I wish to God you'd go away and leave me alone! I've had just about enough ..." A young man in a long overcoat turned round; he was smiling sardonically, ironically, cryptically, just a little sadly and bitterly — Alexey. In the Café Sarnuta, centre of the Bohemia of St Giles, David heard frequent opprobrious references to a certain young Russian named Alexis, who smoked cigarettes through a holder a foot long and stared at one through narrowed eyelids. David did not need to turn round when someone said: "Look! There he is! Let's pretend we haven't seen him...." Alexey strolled through the café alone, always alone, smiling, pouting his lips, turning his head from side to side and flinging it back to redispose the two loose waves of his hair round its centre parting.

Then David did not see Alexey for ten years. He heard how Alexey had volunteered for the army on the first day of the war in order to spread communism in the ranks; how he had been captured by the Germans and escaped. He read in the newspapers of a certain Alexey Alexandrovich being hooted down at a political meeting in the Midlands. David expected to run into him again in some odd place and at some odd time; to catch a glimpse of him from the top of a bus or to find him sitting in the next seat in a cinema. But in fact the meeting took place at Tony's villa in the suburbs, facing the arterial road.

David arrived first. Tony, the prosperous G.P. of the semi-detached suburb, bustled David into the lounge for a drink, the old wide grin of welcome and general satisfaction covering his face from ear to ear. Tony was so satisfied, and in addition the professional manner had taken possession of him so completely, that he simultaneously rubbed his hands and chuckled, patted David's arm reassuringly and peered into his face, held David by the pulse and said: "Medicine! That's the game you ought to have taken up! Or why not write a best-seller? Look at Aldous Huxley. Look at Gerald Kersh! What was he? Just an ordinary Jewish fellah. Live! Live! Here, wait a minute —" Tony dashed out to his car, ostensibly to retrieve a packet of cigarettes, but really, David felt sure, to give himself a chance to slam the car-door, because he loved slamming the car-door more than anything else in the world. Having slammed it once, he pretended to himself that it had not closed properly in order to open it and slam it again.

The lounge in Tony's villa had a small bay-window. Tony and David stood there, as they used to stand in Meresham Road, looking out on the colourless front-gardens, the empty footway, and the arterial road beyond. There was only one person in sight, a shortish man wearing a bowler hat and carrying a neatly rolled umbrella. He drew nearer, and as he walked up the little drive leading into Tony's villa David recognised that it was Alexey.

Alexey had, inevitably, been excommunicated from "the party", but he had also, less inevitably, experienced a change of heart. What his new political views, if any, were, David did not discover; but whatever they were, Alexey was now modest, polite, considerate, almost humble. He was working for a firm of brokers on the Stock Exchange. "Much maligned people, stockbrokers," he said. "They're good chaps, most of them ... You know, I've come to the conclusion that what matters chiefly about people is what they're like as people, whether they've got good hearts and standards, and so on. Of course, as you both know, I've done all sorts of things and had all sorts of ups and downs, but I've been able to learn ... and go on learning..."

PART EIGHT
POETS

1

O N SUNDAYS, the streets west of Aldgate were empty
and clean. Towards evening there was not a soul
to be seen, except a tall constable of the City of
London police walking calmly and softly beside the grey,
dignified buildings. The sky was grey, the massive stone
thoroughfares were grey, but without despair. Among the
variations of grey ran a thread of dark-blue which spread,
after rain, in thin glistening sheets over the pavements.
At dusk, yellow lamps were lit, illuminating courtyards
and alleyways, splaying out their light evenly and regu-
larly along the wet roadways.

Here, one autumn, David began to take long,
exploratory Sunday walks. They had the reflective peace,
the recuperative, sober beauty of a walk through wet
countryside. He registered vistas and scenes and
absorbed a fine, distilled atmosphere of the past. He went
through the lists of occupants in the doorways of office
buildings and took pleasure in the impressive solidity of
their names. He looked out for the blue plaques which
announced, in the deserted dusk, that Chaucer or
Johnson, Milton or Keats had once lived where this bank
or that post office now stood. He wandered on curiously
through Bread Alleys and Pudding Lanes and sections of
Watling Street, peopling the incomparable square mile
with a composite population drawn from two thousand
years; Romans and medieval merchants, seventeenth-
century playwrights and eighteenth-century wits were

hazily and romantically mixed, until he found himself at the end of the Strand.

The present re-asserted itself. Beyond Aldwych the neon signs were lit, the streets were full of traffic and the pavements crowded. But that territory remained unexplored. It was time for him to catch the bus home, to have tea, and to do the week-end homework which had been postponed to the very last hour.

The experience of beauty had to be shared. David invited his classmate Stanley to accompany him on his walks through the City and by the Thames. They talked a great deal and found that they were both poets. Stanley discovered T.S. Eliot, and they recited "The Waste Land" to each other. Very soon they began to recite their own poems, about streets and bridges, about railways and suburbs and rain.

"The wind lashes briskly
Each cold, coloured cheek,
The rain blinds the eyes
And silvers the pavement
With the wet, naked cold
Of the night.
Lamp-posts and taxis
Spray light on the streets,
The gutters rush torrents
Of intertwined cables
And cargoes of matchsticks ..."

Their poems had the determined, unhesitating melancholy of adolescence and they returned home very content.

The following autumn they responded to the lure of those neon-lit streets which lay beyond Aldwych. Instead of catching the bus back safely to tea and homework and to the composition of further poems about suburbs and rain and the call of railway engines in the night, they found themselves drifting with uneasy excitement up the

166

Strand and into Leicester Square. They examined the covers of magazines at bookstalls which stayed open late and walked past stout women ambling up and down back-streets till they reached the wholly fascinating land of Soho. Moisture covered the windows of cafés into which they scarcely dared look, in case they should be set upon by the gangsters of whom they had read in the Sunday newspapers. They pushed past the vendors of roasted chestnuts and peanuts, oranges, movie-magazines, and gewgaws; they brushed the evening newspapers of idlers who leaned against walls eternally scanning the back-page racing forecasts; they hastily glanced down into heavily bolted basements labelled "Sam's" or "The Rumba Club". They were enchanted. This was an urban fairy-land.

Late one evening, bold and emancipated, their school-caps stuffed out of sight into overcoat pockets, they entered an Italian café, and in the furthest corner table ordered small white coffees. They sat, saying nothing, scarcely looking or listening, nourishing themselves on the purest air of romance. Soon the clock showed mid-night. Should they stay there for ever? In the last resort, they were too sensible, so they walked along Old Compton Street, as populated and animated as three hours before, and caught a late bus to Hackney.

The Italian café was safe; it was open to the street and a great crowd was always massed outside and over-flowed on to the kerb. But there were other cafés which beckoned sinisterly and irresistibly and which they had not the nerve to enter. What went on behind the impen-etrable curtain of moisture which covered their glass fronts? Sometimes they heard music coming from them, strange, heart-stirring music of the accordeon and the guitar. And once, standing in the rainy street on a black winter's night, they listened to a young boy singing in a café labelled "Budetti's". He sang a song they had never heard before, a wonderful, simple, and touching melody — "Santa Luccia". The scene and the music created in

167

Stanley's mind almost at once the words of a small poem:

"Black night and the rain was falling,
From a café in Babylon
I heard a boy's voice calling:
    'Come back to Santa Luccia,
    Oh, come back to Santa Luccia!'
London was black and the rain
Was the grief and tears of the world,
And the voice was calling again:
    'Come back to Santa Luccia,
    Oh, come back to Santa Luccia!'"

Their next step to the heart of the mystery was to enter a café in Frith Street whose windows were only half steamed up with moisture and into which it was just possible to see. What they saw was a row of empty tables, a small old man reading a newspaper at one end, and a fat woman brooding over a tea-cup at the other. The place seemed harmless enough, though they knew that such seeming innocence was probably only a blind. However, since ostensibly it invited bona fide customers, and since they were not, after all, complete funks, they went in. They looked neither to right nor left, they hesitated about a table, dithered half-way, and then carried on boldly to the furthest corner table, as usual. The atmosphere was electric; they did not turn round, but they sensed it. From secret panels in the wall, they knew, foreigners of no conceivable nationality were peering at them, fingering knives, mixing potions, poisons, crazy stupefiants, and aphrodisiacs. These foreigners knew all about them, in a way; one of their infinitely cunning, almost invisible agents had probably trailed them here from Hackney. But knowing who David and Stanley were did not satisfy them that the two boys were up to no mischief. They were watching. At any moment, the blow, the unimaginable blow would fall.

"Two small white coffees, please," said Stanley. The unseen watchers of no conceivable nationality were shocked; so these two nosy kids had the nerve to ask for coffees, did they!

The coffees arrived, they drank, they smoked a Turkish cigarette apiece. No knife-blade whizzed suddenly across the back of their necks; no weird, horrible sensation resulted from drinking the small cupfuls of coffee, no one said anything, no one asked any questions, nothing happened. They were reassured, they were gaining ground. They took another Turkish cigarette apiece from their joint packet. What exoticism emanated from the pungent smoke of their cigarettes! What a mysterious, cosmopolitan aura pervaded their corner of the little Soho café! Stanley took from his pocket a copy of Baudelaire's poems and began calmly to read, every now and again repeating aloud a line which was wonderfully appropriate to their mood. David followed suit and brought out his Verlaine.

"Two more small white coffees, please!" David called with assurance to the waitress.

"Listen," said Stanley:

"In fading streets of aged capitals,
Where even horror turns to enchantment,
I watch, obedient to my fatal moods,
Curious people, broken-down and charming."

David listened, remaining for some moments with his ear cocked attentively towards Stanley. The coffee urn hissed, a barrel-organ played in the street. Then it was David's turn:

"Still the river flows, and twisting and turning
Drags through Paris its old snake's body:
Old, muddy snake, bearing to its wharves
Cargoes of wood, of oil — and of corpses!"

"Teeming city!" — said Stanley — "City crowded with dreams! Where ghosts in broad daylight brush the passer-by...."

2

DAVID AND Stanley made the Café Mirandella their headquarters and began to "drop in", as they put it, whenever they were within three or four miles of Soho. They came almost every Saturday night so that — though they lived in neighbouring districts, a long bus ride was necessary in order to bring about such a chance meeting — they might "run into each other" at Mirandella's. Stanley spent the afternoon in the gallery of a theatre, pottered around Charing Cross Road for a bit, and then settled down, with a packet of Turkish cigarettes and a paper-covered book of French poems, to wait for David at Mirandella's.

One Saturday night Stanley failed to turn up. David was puzzled and disturbed, because they had agreed to "run into each other" at the café in Frith Street. His absence spoiled the entire evening. The café seemed empty and cold, which in fact it was. Moreover, it was Stanley who bought the packet of Turkish cigarettes, whose cost they afterwards shared. An hour passed, two hours. From time to time David went into the slightly foggy street, torn with neon lighting — "Wounds of the fog are bleeding" — looked up and down, and even squeezed into the Italian café on the other side of the road. But Stanley was not to be seen. Back in Mirandella's, David turned uneasily to Verlaine.

"In the old park, lonely and frozen,
A man and a woman are walking slowly.

170

Their eyes are veiled, their lips are soft
And their words in the dusk can scarcely be heard.

'Do you remember our love in the old days?'
'Why should I? What is there to remember?' "

Perhaps something was wrong; maybe something had happened to Stanley here in Soho. They had recently begun to take the district's sinister reputation lightly. This, possibly, was the evening for which its inner denizens — those foreigners of extraordinary cosmopolitan origin and no conceivable nationality — had been waiting. If so, what should he say to Stanley's mother? In principle, when they came to Mirandella's, they were out for a long walk looking at the shops and things... "So those are the shops you look at!" David could hear her say. "Dirty filthy cafés in the West End! And now where is my poor boy! My poor lost boy!"

" 'Do you remember our love in the old days?'
'Why do you expect me to remember?' "

"In the old park, lonely and frozen,
Two ghosts are walking slowly."

Suddenly, the stale, moribund café was brought to life by the entry of Stanley. The door opened and slammed to violently, excited steps sounded over the wooden floorboards, Stanley flopped into the chair opposite David, and stared deeply into vacancy, chin on left hand, right leg sprawled out beyond the table.

"What's the matter?" said David. "Where have you been?"

Stanley said nothing. He had a taste for the dramatic and prolonged the silence and the posture. He seemed all right, however. His eyes shone with news and sensation rather than catastrophe.

"Got the cigarettes?" said David, preparing to savour

171

the situation in its appropriate Turkish aroma. Stanley brought out the packet with his right hand, leaving his position undisturbed, and shook out a cigarette. There were only four left! What on earth had he been up to? Still using only one hand, he lit himself a cigarette, too, and finally looked at David with drooping eyes.

"Listen," he said. He recited several stanzas.

"Now I leave you
And I kiss you
This night is over.
I must wander
Slowly homeward
By the river.

I shall linger so
In memory
For ever...."

David remained for some moments, as usual, with his ear cocked attentively towards Stanley. "I like it," said David finally.

"I made it up just now," said Stanley significantly.

"You mean —?"

"Yes."

Stanley told David what had happened. He had been standing in the gallery queue for his customary Saturday afternoon visit to the theatre. A girl had been standing next to him. They had talked; they had sat next to each other in the gallery. Afterwards they had had tea together. And after that they had gone for a walk, for hours and hours, up and down the Embankment from Blackfriars to Chelsea. He knew only her first name, Louise. She was French and on a visit to England. She was fifteen, just a year older than Stanley. Beneath Big Ben, as the clock struck eleven, she had said she must go. Stanley had wanted that they should correspond and meet again. But she had said no, it was

172

better that their evening together should be unique, that they should know nothing further of each other, in the past or in the future, that they should retain only a single memory of an evening when they were young. So they had kissed very quickly on Westminster Bridge and walked off in different directions as fast as they could without turning round. That, said Stanley, was why he had failed to arrive at the café, and that was the explanation of his poem.

The encounter was placed in a special category. It was put at David's disposal, as though he too had been present. They often referred to it when discussing girls.

"Like Louise, for instance," one of them would say to illustrate a point.

"Yes, for example like Louise."

3

I T WAS not until the following summer that David had a similar experience, less substantial, but no less memorable, and equally the occasion for a poem. Stanley and David went to Southend for the day, on their own. They found a rather abandoned waste-land of a beach towards Shoeburyness. The book they took with them was *From Montmartre to the Latin Quarter*, recollections of the underworld and Bohemia by Francis Carco. It was a delightful book and what pleased them most were the scraps of verse, borrowed from poets, café-singers, and forgotten composers of doggerel, which formed a harmonious and integral part of the text.

"O my beautiful boat, O memory
Have we sailed enough?"

asked Francis Carco in recalling his youthful Bohemia. But before long he would be quoting advice and information in another vain:

"Take the bus, don't go by tube
You can never be too careful"

Or:

"It's the sort of music that kills....
in the end you get used to it."

Or (though this did not actually appear in the book):

"Take a seat; if there isn't one, sit on the floor.
And if you want to speak, begin by shutting up."

They lay on the beach, sunbathing and taking turns in reading *From Montmartre to the Latin Quarter,* with the salty smell of the sea around them, mixed with the fumes of the Shoeburyness brick works. David suggested a swim, but Stanley preferred to read; so David left him to take a bathe on his own. It was low tide and the sea was over a mile and a half away. By the time David reached it, the people on the beach formed no more than a thin, broken, dark line beneath the distant silhouette of houses. And though from the beach there had seemed to be quite a number of tiny figures bathing or running about, they turned out to be so widely scattered over the stretches of sand and mud and low water that he found himself alone. Or almost alone; because half a mile or so further out to sea a single figure was wading and plunging ahead in an attempt to reach water deep enough for swimming. David followed.

The sounds of the holiday thousands on the shore were quite lost in space. Out in the shallow sea there was solitude and a silence broken only by the steady movement of David's legs through the water. He ploughed on. The

174

figure in front of him, which was, he saw, wearing an orange bathing costume, ploughed on too. Then it faltered, and finally stopped. David guessed that it had stopped not so much because the water was getting deep — it reached still only just above the waist — but because the stillness and emptiness of those stretches of shallow sea and sand were, after the crowded beaches, almost eerie. He drew nearer to the figure in the orange bathing costume. It was a girl, a very young girl, of about David's own age, and to him a very beautiful girl, though it would have been impossible to make any objective assessment of her beauty. Out there, in space, what were the standards of comparison? They were to all intents and purposes alone amid the vastness of nature. David drew nearer. Convention, too, counted for little in those solitudes. He did what he would never have done inland — he entered into unblushing conversation with a beautiful girl of his own age, a stranger.

"Hey!" he shouted. "Is the tide going in or out?"

"I don't know," she said. "You have to be careful when you're far out because it comes in quickly."

Yes, she was lovely; all the more so because of the cheap, coarse-textured, orange costume which covered her scarcely developed body, and the shapeless, flattened Cockney accents in which she spoke. They waded on, talking occasionally about the tide or swimming or Southend. Once, when she thought she had stepped on a crab, they held hands. Then they swam out together. Everything and everybody was miles away. It seemed that they were out there for hours, swimming and wading. Eventually they turned back. They immersed themselves for the last time and splashed on to the stretches of wet sand and mud. They ran, they raced up and down the soft-ribbed flats. Imperceptibly they moved nearer to the shore. A few other figures approached out of space. The thin black line of people on the beach became distinguishable as separate groups and individuals. They remembered who they were, where they came from, and the fact that they were strangers. They said that they had better be getting back. The tide crept in, swiftly covering the flat stretches with the merest sheet of water. They charted their position in relation to their respective beaches: hers was towards the pier, David's towards Shoeburyness. They began to run again. Gradually, without either of them saying anything, their paths diverged, until David realised that he was running quite alone, with a vast, empty stretch of sand separating him from that other running figure in the orange bathing costume. He slowed down to a walk, every now and again turning round to see if he could still distinguish the girl's distant running figure among the others which dotted the wet sand. He did not make straight for the beach where Stanley was waiting, but walked parallel to the shore until he had composed some verses. When he was ready to tell Stanley the news, it was well past tea-time. A black bank of cloud was massing on the horizon to blot out the sun. David was cold and shivering slightly. The tide was coming in fast and people were leaving the beaches.

"Stanley," he said, as he sank beside his friend on the fly-ridden sand littered with newspaper and bottles, discarded tins and half-eaten sandwiches:

"There is a murmuring on the wide-strewn stones,
There is a melancholy on the lapping sea,
A mourning song which the ocean moans,
As the cold waves break insistently
And the last light fades in gold-black tones...."

4

AFTER A time Stanley and David became disillusioned with the Café Mirandella. What was the point of sitting in there? It was dim, draughty, and empty. Nobody ever came in, nothing ever happened. But over the road there was a most intriguing little place with tubular chairs and chromium fittings and a neat, elegant neon sign outside which said, sufficiently, in small handwritten lettering: "terry's". The windows were not steamed up and the place was not in the least bit sinister, but it was mysterious — or, rather, intriguing, most intriguing. The interior was hidden by discreet curtaining. But when the door opened, there could be seen, perhaps, one dark, sleek-haired man seated on a high stool by the coffee-bar; and at the corner table, two astonishingly elegant and ravishingly beautiful young women smoking cigarettes through brightly-carmined lips. Once again, as at the Mirandella, the remainder of the café was empty throughout the evening. Here, the emptiness was less surprising, because "terry's" was really very small. It was little more than half a room and contained only four black-topped tables, half-a-dozen tubular chairs, and a diminutive bar with three high tubular stools in front of it.

The proprietor's attitude to his café was ambiguous. On the one hand, the discreet curtains, the suave fittings, and the extraordinarily glossy young women seemed to be aiming at an exclusive and expensive clientele. On the other hand, there was the proprietor's personal, smiling welcome to anyone, no matter how scruffy, who hesitated on the iron grating outside. He did not actually say anything, but he inclined his head in so charming, handsome, and glittering a smile that it was equivalent to a spoken invitation to enter. The proprietor spent many hours, almost whole evenings, at the door of his café, radiating positive well-being, charm, and elegance up and down

Frith Street. "terry" had a thin-juanesque moustache, black hair rippled by a few lazy, well-disciplined waves, and a face that was handsome, plump, smooth, and radically pleased with itself and everything else. He was always, to use quite inadequate, routine phrases, "well-groomed", "faultlessly dressed" in "impeccable taste". His clothes had the genuine and restrained perfection of St. James's, with just a suggestion of Old Compton Street dash. Usually his long, sunny, contemplative waitings in the doorway were rewarded by the arrival of a friend in a large car. To celebrate the occasion, "terry" waved and laughed and invited him into the café and they sat with the two astonishingly elegant and ravishingly beautiful young women, all chatting and reminiscing gaily, frequently in French or Italian. These two young women might appear to be the same as the two who had sat at the corner table the previous night, or the night before that, but they were not necessarily so. They were equally elegant, equally beautiful, very similar indeed, but not necessarily identical. There appeared to be somewhere a plentiful supply of them, from which central source two were selected or chose themselves on any particular evening to sit in "terry's". However, it did not matter which two were there, because "terry" knew them all, and to them he introduced his friend with the car, whom he had not seen all these years, and they chatted and reminisced gaily in French or Italian. Then they grew tired of just sitting there, drinking coffee. So they all got up, glossy and perfumed, and drove off in the car, laughing and chatting merrily.

Stanley and David had time to observe these frequent reunions, because for several months they sat on the high stools facing "terry's" coffee-bar, instead of in the Mirandella. Any doubts they had had about entering were set aside by "terry's" smiling charm as they hesitated on the grating outside. They did not feel it appropriate to draw out paper-bound volumes of French poems from their pockets, but instead stared at them-

178

selves in the mirror behind the bar, murmured quietly and discreetly to each other, and glanced at the evening paper. They were intrigued by the café and by the personality of "terry". The mystery, if there was a mystery, remained unsolved, "terry", they heard later, was deported as an undesirable. It was also said that he was an Italian fascist. But these rumours could be the basis only for very ordinary guessing as to what motives were active behind his suave and handsome exterior. Fundamentally he remained a man of deep, unresolved mystery.

Once "terry" and his companions had gone, the café was silent and abandoned. A little time was necessary for some sort of animation, of an altogether more banal and inferior kind, to be re-established by its other permanent occupant. The dark, sleek-haired man seated on a high stool by the coffee bar, and whose back could be seen from the street whenever the door opened, was not, of course, "terry". "terry's" proper place was in the doorway, or at the corner table, or in one of his friends' cars. The permanent occupant of one of the three high stools was a gentleman named Tino: definitely "gentleman", since that was the word Tino himself always used to describe a male person, no matter of what age or class: likewise, "lady" described any female person. His approach to people was oblique and discreet. It was a long time before he addressed Stanley and David directly. Instead, after speaking to the lady behind the bar — the waitress, in fact — he glanced at them in the mirror for support: "I think these gentlemen will agree with what I'm saying," he said to their reflections in the mirror. They nodded vigorously at this slight opening. "Oh yes," they agreed in support of whatever boring law he was laying down. "Most definitely." Then, realising that this was being unchivalrous towards the lady behind the bar, they added: "Though of course there is the other side of the question."

"True," said Tino to their obsequiously grinning reflections, "but I think this lady will grant me the point ..." So it went on for several weeks, "ladys" and "gentlemens" being bandied about, mostly via the mirror, till they and the lady behind the bar, who disappeared into the kitchen with her knitting as often as she could, were quite befuddled with his views on every trivial subject under the sun.

However, when they got to know him better, they found Tino far from being a bore. In fact, as he told himself, he was really "one of the boys". He was a waiter by profession. The difficulty of pinning him down on *when* he waited — since he spent, as far as they could judge, the whole afternoon and evening in "terry's" and other cafés — was complicated by the fact that he was often unemployed.

"I'm working a twelve-hour day —"

"But you were in here all last week."

"I know. I was out of a job."

"And today?"

"My day off."

If he was so often out of work, it was asked, how did he manage to dress so well?

"I make do," said Tino. "Look!" He pulled a coloured silk handkerchief from his overcoat pocket. It had torn edges. "Took this from one of my landlady's cushions. See? Things like that."

He was born of a Greek father and a Mexican mother on the high seas. He said that he had no nationality, no parents, no home, no friends, no wife, and no money. He changed his lodgings every few weeks. If anyone wanted to find him, they could do so at "terry's". He also had his letters delivered there. This struck Stanley and David as an excellent idea. If only they could think of someone to write to them c/o "terry's". In the end they left one or two notes for each other — "Sorry, can't come tomorrow night" or "What's the maths homework?" Tino was not curious, but in due course he asked very casually what they "did".

"We're ... er ..."

180

"... students."

"Oh." Tino was respectful. So they were "wide boys", young though they were, and knew how to get by without working.

"Good luck to you, that's what I say. If you can get away with it, why not?" Then, evidence of his omniscience: "I thought you were, somehow. I thought you were something like that. Students, ay.... Oxford, I suppose?"

"No ... er ..."

"... London."

"Oh. London College?"

"Yes ... er ..."

"... London University."

"Well, good luck to you, that's what I say."

In the last resort, Tino was no fool. It took him some time to come to the point, but eventually he did.

"Look here," he said, after they had been visiting "terry's" for some time and were sick and tired of the place, "why do you come here?"

"Well, we ... er ..."

"... just drop in ..."

"... on our way ..."

"But you gentlemen don't live round here, or anything. I mean, what's the point? Are you writing a book about Soho?"

"Well ... er ..."

"... in a way."

"Ah, I thought so," said Tino triumphantly. "I thought so somehow. I thought you were doing something like that. What are you, writers, artists?"

"We're ... er ..."

"... poets."

"Poets, ay!" Tino was delighted. "This isn't the place you want. You're wasting your time here. You want the Café Sarnuta. Come with me."

He immediately led the way out of "terry's", through some back turnings, and into Charing Cross Road.

"Never been to the Café Sarnuta?" he said. "You've

181

been wasting your time. That's the place you want. Artists, bohemians, writers, they all go there. Yes, that's the place you've been looking for."

They went down a couple of alleyways, turned past the doorway of a dilapidated warehouse, pushed apart some curtains, and found themselves in a sort of a dim cellar with a counter at the end. When their eyes had adjusted themselves to the semi-darkness, they agreed that this was indeed the place they had been looking for. There were two men with beards, several men with long hair, a girl with short hair, paintings on the walls, a couple playing chess, someone strumming a ukulele ... Tino sat with them for a couple of minutes at one of the obscurer tables; then, having done his good turn — it was not necessary to order anything in this café — went back to "terry's". They were left with the Café Sarnuta at their disposal, there to be bored poetically to their hearts' content.

"When falls the dusk, erotic hour,
Rises the yellow crescent moon;
Soft awakening, twilit hour...
Death the mistress will come soon."

5

THE CAFÉ Sarnuta was an informal café, restaurant, and community centre which thrived on atmosphere and imagination. It was a little corner of make-believe set among the dark back-streets of St. Giles. As such it suited their purpose admirably. In it they read and composed their poems, sinking deeper and deeper, at weekends and on occasional evenings, into a despair that nevertheless appeared most attractive, significant, and full of charm. Walking up from

Hackney, through Islington and Clerkenwell, along
narrow streets, like canyons, lined with tenements, and
past straggling rows of stalls, whose yellow flares
impinged fiercely and ineffectually upon the surrounding fog and rain and darkness, they remembered the
"Song of the Ill-loved" by Guy Apollinaire:

> "One night of fog in London
> A ruffian who resembled
> My sweetheart came towards me
> And the look in his unknown eyes
> Made me lower my head with shame ...
>
> I saw his inhuman stare
> The scar at his open neck
> He staggered drunk from a pub
> At the moment when I recognised
> The falsity of love itself."

Associated with the Café Sarnuta was a basement club
next door called Ronnie's, whose despairful members sat
by the light of candles and listened to the Soho accor-
dionists rend from their banal, tragic instruments a late
night rhythmic discord of tangos, javas, and paso-dobles.
A huge, fat Spanish woman named Maria played loudest
and best. Her strange and terrible melodies reached a
climax on Saturday nights, when the small, low-
ceilinged room was full and one end of the room was
scarcely visible from the other through the fog of tobacco
smoke. To her David wrote:

> "Play me a tango, Maria,
> On the savage accordion,
> Till it is late
> And the candles gutter,
> Till it is all
> Too late and too much ..."

no one liked their poems, which after a time were mostly torn up and thrown away. Only their school-friend Tony, a most unliterary person, remembered what they had written. The three friends had formed and maintained the habit of eating in Soho on Christmas Eve. At first they ate in a very cheap Italian place where spaghetti was served in enamel bowls on bare wooden tables and where they afterwards luxuriated reflectively over a six-penny glass of chianti and half a cigar. Tony, gay, bubbling, and boastful, had at first listened to their poems with a condescending and pitying admiration. But he remembered them. Eventually they held their dinners on Christmas Eve in expensive little restaurants with fresh bowls of flowers on white tablecloths and champagne fizzing in thin-stemmed wine-glasses. Stanley and David listened uneasily and then with strange enthusiasm as scarcely recognisable scraps of poems were quoted back at them and Tony sentimentalised about the past. "Those poems of yours I shall never forget them. Those were the days," he said.

"My grief is like a river
It flows and does not cease,
It flows among the houses
That whisper each to each ..."

"And how did that French thing go, the one you translated?" he continued relentlessly.

"The long sighs of the violins of autumn
Wound my heart with a monotonous languor.
Overcome and helpless when the hour sounds,
I remember the old days and I cry.
And I drift with the evil wind which carries me
Here and there, like a dead leaf."

After their Christmas Eve dinner they sometimes strolled through St. Giles. A vast block of office buildings rose

from the bombed sites. The Café Sarnuta and the neighbouring basements had vanished. With the old decor
gone, how difficult to recapture the mood of that late
nineteenth-century French poetry which had inspired
their own verses.... Tony, however, recited David's trans-
lation of some lines by Theophile Gautier:

    "All things pass, but art
    Remains to eternity:
    The marble verse
    Survives the city."

PART NINE
THE UTOPIANS

1

IRREGULARLY, by fits and starts, David wandered out of childhood into adolescence. Usually Stanley led the way. It was Stanley who, when they were thirteen years old, first discovered the unabridged and illustrated edition of *Ovid* in the Public Library; then certain revelatory and fascinating photographic magazines; and a little later certain strange, troubling, not wholly comprehensible, yet exciting facts about men and women in which the major role was played by parts of the body whose functions had hitherto appeared simple and trivial. Again, it was Stanley who first discovered the poems of T.S. Eliot; the works of H.G. Wells; and a stout volume called the *Handbook of Marxism* which led him to pay a few romantic, though not in the end satisfying visits to the cellars of the disused synagogue, formerly a Wesleyan chapel, where the young communists had their underground headquarters.

David remembered vaguely the visits to this underground headquarters which he had made some years before in the company of Uncle Jake. But the explorations which he had occasionally shared with Uncle Jake had been confined to Hackney. Stanley went further afield. Unable to swallow the *Handbook of Marxism* in its entirety — the handbook, like a long, cohesive string of inedible food, had to go down whole or not at all — Stanley was presented with an alternative diet, lighter, more varied, and far more digestible. In Hampstead and

Bloomsbury and Charing Cross Road existed a book club, a drama association, a poetry league, a debating society, a social group, and by joining these, without committing himself or accepting in its entirety the long, glutinous string of the *Handbook of Marxism,* he could be associated, freely, with "the movement".

It was Stanley, too, who discovered the weekly magazines, in whose back pages extraordinary names were bandied about: names charged with intimation, names whose significance David did not understand but which suggested, momentarily and bewilderingly, as in flashes of lightning, landscapes of knowledge and experience that had to be investigated. Aldous Huxley was one such name and D.H. Lawrence was another; James Joyce and Bernard Shaw; Bertrand Russell, Proust, Thomas Mann, Freud, Nietzsche, Gandhi, Dostoievski, Schopenhauer — the more foreign the names, the more necessary it became to find out how to pronounce them correctly and to what secrets they were the key. What was psychoanalysis and what was the life force? What was empiricism and who was Stephen Daedalus? Who was the Superman and what in heaven's name was metaphysics? Some of these mysteries seemed even more curiously inaccessible than others. David asked the librarian if he could borrow a book called *Ulysses* and she said that it was banned, her manner suggesting that in asking for the book he had committed a faux pas or used some slightly indecent expression. And when both Stanley and David asked one of the younger masters what *Lady Chatterley's Lover* was about, he laughed contemptuously and said: "Oh, *that* book. People make such a fuss, and do you know what it's really about? It's nothing more than — No, but I won't tell you. You read it for yourselves and find out." And he lent them his Tauchnitz edition of Lawrence.

Of course, by the time they had reached their first year in the sixth form, they both knew the "facts of life" — or thought they did; they weren't absolutely sure if they had got them right — but they couldn't make out what all the extra fuss was about, the volumes and volumes of books on the subject, the lectures to which only those over eighteen were admitted, the secrets, the reticences, and many of the jokes. The "facts of life", if they had understood them aright, could surely not fill more than one slim booklet? ... Gradually, however, they managed to form some idea of the immense scope of the whole business. Not that they were very interested at first; not, at any rate, in the theoretical side. But as their adolescence continued, the practical side, when they stopped to think of it, nearly drove them to distraction. They could imagine holding out a few weeks or a few months against the images and desires which began to obsess them. But a year? Two years? Three years! They dared not consider so appalling a prospect: the long, heartbreaking summer evenings when body, heart, and soul yearned for sweet femininity, the urgent nights, the suggestive afternoons; and winter, no less, but only differently, encouraging with its scents and scenes what needed no encouragement; and autumn; and spring ... If now, at the age of fifteen or sixteen, they felt as they did, what would they feel like at the age of eighteen? Fortunately, they thought, at the age of eighteen, when they left school, they would be able, by marriage or otherwise, to resolve the by then inconceivable tension. If they had been told that a further seven or eight years beyond school-leaving age would very likely pass before this tension was effectively reduced, they would have received the news as a man might receive the news that he is to spend ten years in prison or hospital. Long afterwards statistical reports were to reveal to them that their individual experience had been a widespread general experience; and that in this respect the body's chemistry reached its maximum of activity precisely when, as a rule, it had minimum opportunity.

Stanley and David found among the novelists, playwrights, and essayists, teachers to help them through their perplexities. They could still be absolutely certain of nothing, but they were able to follow these teachers along some sort of reasonable path from the fogs of pre-history to what seemed to be the comparative clarity of the late nineteenth century; thence to the bemused — though, they believed, only temporarily bemused — time in which they were actually living. Different kinds of sanity, different kinds of vision, artistic and intellectual, reached them from the shelves of the Hackney Public Library. H.G. Wells and Bernard Shaw, Somerset Maugham and Bertrand Russell, J.B. Priestley and Aldous Huxley, G.K. Chesterton and Oscar Wilde gave them a notion of why things were so, provided them with a framework for their education. The writers indicated to them, also, an indefinable purpose in life: a purpose which was a provisional and ever-changing restatement by great men of their time, with their special knowledge and experience, of what other great men had provisionally stated for other times, with other special knowledge and experience, each with a different emphasis resulting from differences in time, place, and personality.

Stanley it was who discovered H.G. Wells, the first of these writers to influence their education. Stanley was an only child, whose parents lived in a quiet, well-polished little flat in Stoke Newington, in which one room was set aside as Stanley's study. His parents were an easy-going, affectionate, surprisingly youthful Jewish couple who encouraged him to do as he liked. They regretted only that his inclinations were not more hearty and full-bloodedly vulgar. Films, dances, card-playing, billiards, going out with some, nice Jewish girl — they would really have preferred all these to his books, theatre-going, and mysterious sorties into West and North London in the company of David Hirsch. However, apart from some good-natured and light-hearted teasing, they made no criticism and provided him with everything he might need to further his intellectual activities.

189

In his study, then, Stanley had the undisturbed leisure to read widely and thoroughly. In David Hirsch's home, on the other hand, there was usually — even when none of his numerous relatives were present — an atmosphere of comings and goings, meals to be eaten, arguments to be thrashed out, nosyness, distractions, hurly-burly. Some visitor with a beard, bearing still a salty flavour of Bessarabia, perhaps, or Lithuania, or the Ukraine, was as often as not drinking a glass of tea in the kitchen and anxious to engage David in Gogolian discussion. And though David Hirsch eventually had his own little room, neither the room nor his own temperament encouraged him to stay in it for long. He would very soon dash down to the kitchen, stroll out to the Public Library, call on a friend, or play a game of chess. The result was that his reading was nothing like as systematic as Stanley's. Instead, a paragraph, a chapter, a name glimpsed in an article would fertilise his imagination and provide him with wild intuitions which, whether by luck or innate skill, might on occasion prove themselves to be accurate and perceptive.

2

ONE EXCEPTION to David's habit of dipping and browsing and skimming occurred when he heard of H.G. Wells. David was strolling through Ridley Road market towards the end of the first summer holidays after matriculation. The holidays had been luxuriously leisurely. Having matriculated he could, like a man retiring on a comfortable pension, look back with contented detachment on the ardours of his youth. Alternatively, he could look forward: and there stretched a future of unlimited variety and possibility — provided, of course, he ignored the international news. As regards the news, he displayed the same dichotomy as most of his elders showed at that time. On the one hand he believed that war was inevitable, and that, in the age of aeroplanes, high-explosive bombs, and poison gas, it would mean the end of the world as hitherto known. The obvious course therefore was to enjoy to the full the few remaining years of life; which could best be accomplished by pretending that war would never come and that everything was normal. On the other hand, he believed that this was in fact true and that war *would* never come; that in the age of aeroplanes, high-explosive bombs and poison gas, no one, not even Hitler, would dare to begin a major war; that the building up of armed forces and the threats of international diplomacy were an extraordinarily subtle game of bluff; and that the most the armed powers would ever dare would be a few minor skirmishes as token tests of strength and as part of the game of bluff. Again, like many young people, David Hirsch could in any case not really imagine himself living beyond the age of twenty. Where Oscar Wilde had said: "To have reached the age of thirty is to have failed in life," David Hirsch might have said: "To have reached the age of twenty is to have completed the term of life." But simultaneously, in accordance with the dichotomy already mentioned and again like many young people, David Hirsch did not really believe that he would ever die, did not really believe that he would ever grow old, assumed that somehow he was immortal and eternally young. Finally, like many people of all ages, David Hirsch did not think about these matters more than occasionally and as it were abstractedly, as though they did not concern him, but were a vexation that he might read about one day in the newspapers. So, ignoring the news, he was contented, full of excited expectation, and also pleasantly sad. Matriculation had been his objective, beyond which lay paradise. And paradise, even when exactly corresponding in detail to what one had imagined, was, though pleasant enough, not, somehow, paradise.... Feeling pleasantly sad, therefore, David Hirsch strolled among the barrows of Ridley Road market. One day he would be strolling along the boulevards of Paris — or alternatively, according to the dichotomy, he would *never* stroll along the boulevards of Paris; his landscape would *always* be Hackney or Dalston or Dibley, or, after a bus-ride, the West End and slightly more elegant districts of London; he would *always,* on hot, passionate summer afternoons, be kicking his way through discarded cabbage-leaves in London markets. One day there would be walking by his side a sweet and feminine and distinguished, totally sympathetic and alluring person — or alternatively and more probably there would *never* be such a person by his side. Then again, perhaps Hackney was the best place after all: to know everybody, to be going back to school in a couple of weeks ... the school library, the cosy winter evenings, games of fives, the dramatic society, the debating society, the week-ends, the jaunts through the City and the West End.... Strolling along in this sad-happy mood, David Hirsch caught sight of Stanley coming towards him and carrying a large, ochre-bound library book. The sight of his friend produced a thrill of agreeable familiarity. Now for a good old chin-wag, he thought.

"See this?" said Stanley, pointing to the book. The cover said simply *Autobiography,* and below that, Wells, and below that D 15672.

"Don't you remember?" said Stanley. David *did* remember. He had already, at Stanley's suggestion, read a couple of Wells's novels. "This tells you all about his life. Everything. All about his childhood and the people he's met and the things he's done. Look." Stanley pointed out a couple of passages dealing with Wells's life at their own age. "And look here." He pointed to a photograph of Wells in his sixties. "And look at these." These were humorous doodlings and verses. "He lives by Regent's Park, you know. Hanover Terrace. I've got the number: I looked it up in the phone-book. It's wonderful, I'm half-way through it now."

"Have they got another copy in the library?" asked David.

They straightaway went to borrow another copy of the *Autobiography,* and during the next couple of days paid several visits to each other's houses to let each other know which page they had reached, to recapitulate passages, and to find analogies between the lives of people in the book and the lives of themselves and their acquaintances. David Hirsch became an even more devoted reader of Wells than Stanley. Previously David's favourite author had been P.G. Wodehouse, in spite of the attempt by a classmate named Eliahu Bogoljuborovitz to convert him to Stephen Leacock. Now, after a first reading of the *Autobiography,* he read steadily and in sequence the novels of the first period; the scientific tales; the social novels written before 1914; the novels written during the First World War and shortly after; the volumes of essays, speeches, ideas, and theories with their scientific, utopian, educational, controversial, and political themes; then the enormous triology of *The Outline of History, The Science of Life,* and *The Work, Wealth, and Happiness of Mankind.* He continued with the short stories, the novels and essays of the 1920s and the 1930s, *The Shape of Things to Come,* and whatever he could lay his hands on in the way of newspaper articles, interviews, or pieces of writing of any kind written by or about Wells. He even read the little science text-book written by one H.G. Wells, B.Sc., when the author was a correspondence-school teacher. David Hirsch, fancying that he might be the only person other than Wells himself to have read every one of these works through conscientiously from cover to cover, thought that this might qualify him to write the first comprehensive study of the author and his works; but came to the disappointing conclusion that many other Wellsians must already have had the same idea.... He found that there already existed a bibliography of Wells's writings; and a biography by Geoffrey West.

David Hirsch was from the outset no completely uncritical admirer of Wells; and in later years he found still more to criticise. But he did not forget that Wells had been his pre-eminent teacher and friend. The very ideas, the very standards, the very temper which Wells had been first to inculcate led him to question the master. And that, surely, was what the master, all the great masters, would have wished? The external form which ideas took, the dogma as it were, was bound to change from generation to generation and vary from individual to individual in accordance with experience and personality; might, at certain points, be the exact opposite of what it was at other points; but the spirit — multitudinously diverse though it was, and irreconcilably chaotic though it might appear — which shaped the external form, and which formulated the dogma, was, among men of goodwill, the same. Thus, David Hirsch rejected, not so much H.G. Wells's science as its scientists; but perhaps the master, had he lived fifty years later, would have done the same, and with the full vigour of his intellect and imagination?

Some disillusionment came. Biographers set Wells in the context of his time and he no longer cut so confident a figure. The style was the man, and the style included those paragraphs and books which repeated indefinitely their own self-perpetuating jargon. The despair of his dying years laid bare half his work. Yet when all reservations and criticisms had been made, H.G. Wells remained the man who had prophetically indicated more of what was significantly happening in the world of his time than any single other; though of course the ideas of no single individual, however great, weighed more than a little beside the collective wisdom of his time. H.G. Wells remained for David a phenomenon of intellect and imagination, any one part of whose manifold work would have been enough to establish the greatness of another man: the youthful comic novels, the scientific and prophetic tales, the utopian and educational writings, the controversies, always rumbustious, always stimulating, the outstanding social novels.... He was Wells.

3

FROM WELLS the two sixth-formers went on to Bertrand Russell, and from Bertrand Russell to the general text-books of philosophy, which brought them to that first crossroads in philosophical speculation, the crossroads which experienced travellers shun but to which they find themselves unwillingly returning from time to time: the confused and irresoluble crossroads of free-will and determinism. Everything has a cause, and that cause has a cause, and that cause has a cause; nothing is causeless. Then surely the ultimate cause or causes have already determined what is now happening and what will happen? If everything is predetermined, then what is the point of life other than a mere effecting of causes? What values can there be if all actions are merely the inevitable effect of unknown previous causes; if choice is an illusion and life is but the working out of predetermined inevitability? If on the other hand, somehow, incomprehensibly, causes do not produce logically and inevitably the effects, however complicated and unanticipated, which must result from them, why then, results are arbitrary and capricious and life still more pointless. So they reasoned, and their conclusions made David Hirsch feel miserable, as though his stomach were weighted down with lead. Stanley did not seem to mind so much; in fact he took delight in demonstrating the inescapable logic of determinism.

Adults, David thought, do not as a rule care if life is determined, do not care even if it is pointless — although he granted that it was possible to hold that life was determined without necessarily holding that it was pointless: one might recognise fate, recognise what those who believed in God would call the will of God and feel that so far from this fate, this will, being pointless, it was the only point. Adults seemed to be so preoccupied with living, with responding to day-to-day and year-to-year stimuli and stresses, that they usually snorted in disgust or shrugged their shoulders at the questions: Has life a point? If it has, what is the point? Or they might have despaired of finding an answer to those questions and wished simply to carry on as peacefully as possible till death released them from the pointless pleasures and pains of life. Or they might have found a satisfactory or semi-satisfactory answer in one of the formal religions or philosophical systems. In any case, they did not seem to care urgently; the questions did not keep them awake o' nights. The very young, on the other hand, frequently did care, greatly, passionately, about the point of life. For a brief period, it was all important to them, more important than sex, vanity, ambition, fear. They wanted life to be — in some unseizable artistic, logical, or moral sense — perfect, coherent; and before they could even begin to find perfection, they had to have a point ... David Hirsch was himself for a time one of these philosophically passionate youngsters. During the months of early summer, he worried about determinism. It hung like a dark cloud over the early part of his third term in the sixth form.

Stanley, though less involved, stood by. One torrid Friday afternoon in June, the sixth form debated the question. Some yawned and grinned and dozed; others listened in blank bewilderment; the active metaphysicians were divided into two groups. One group was positively, joyously, fervently deterministic. Everything, they argued, was settled, and the result was science and socialism, and what more could one ask? Determinism put the teachers and parents in their places. Their opponents argued that a determined life in a deterministic world would be intolerable. Since determinism was intolerable, therefore it could not be true.

David Hirsch found both arguments unsatisfactory. Determinism seemed to be the logical conclusion of rational thought. Yet, not only was it intolerable, but it conflicted with common sense. Common sense knew, though it could not explain, that there existed choice; that choice, chance, possibility, and probability existed side by side with logical determinism. Again, he rejected the arguments of the exponents of free will. Determinism might be most unpleasant — he was loth to say intolerable; a situation could be most unpleasant, yet, if people did in fact tolerate it, still, barely, tolerable — or even, for the sake of argument, actually intolerable; but it might none the less be true. A man informed that he is suffering from a painful and fatal illness might find the statement intolerable, might refuse to accept it; yet it might still be objectively true at the time. The tolerability or otherwise of a statement did not change its objective truth at the time, though it might change it later.

When school was over, a knot of excited logicians remained in the classroom to continue the discussion. Then, one by one, they drifted off. The form-master looked in to say that he was going home: would the last to leave lock the door and hand the key to the porter. In the end David and Stanley were alone. They could not bring themselves to abandon the subject until it had been decided one way or the other. Half-a-dozen philosophical text-books lay on the table, open at the chapter on determinism. The sun shone, broad and golden, on to the school playground. The last homegoing schoolboys straggled towards the gates or, with one foot on the pedal, propelled their bicycles down the cycle path, and swinging on to the saddle shot along the drive. The heat of the day was over, and the first hour of evening was sweet and perfect. But for David the sweetness and perfection were a mockery if, deterministically, from cause to effect, life were decided, unalterable, and doomed.

Suddenly the crisis had passed, never to return. David Hirsch saw that determinism, in proving its conclusion, destroyed its premises; as though an army, advancing into and occupying an enemy country, found that its own country had simultaneously been entered and occupied by the seemingly defeated enemy. Determinism proved that all judgments were determined, including, therefore, the judgment that all judgments were determined. What greater validity had this judgment than its opposite: that all judgments were not determined? ... But really it was impossible to think on those lines at all. The mind simply could not, as one book put it, lift itself up, any more than a man could take himself by the coat collar and raise himself from the ground; though, if strong enough, he could raise another man from the ground.

Stanley tentatively agreed, pleased, for the moment, with David's logic. In fact, said Stanley, the mind, while legitimately reaching out into the furthest remoteness, had to be based on terra firma. That terra firma was the free judgment. If the free judgment made use of its freedom to decide that it was not free, then it had reached a circular argument from which it had to withdraw, accepting, for ordinary life, the limited determinism of common sense, and for philosophical speculation the existence of irresoluble mystery.

Yes, said David, and returned to his metaphor of the armies: philosophical speculation could send out strong probing expeditions of reasoned enquiry and logical exploration into enemy territory, but it could not effectively and substantially occupy that territory without necessarily bringing about the enemy occupation of its own country. Nor could it even exchange its own country for the enemy's, because only its own country could furnish it with essential supplies.

That night David and Stanley walked far, freed of their

198

burden, enjoying, gently and afresh, the visible world. They walked through the sad and oppressive, yet strangely beautiful streets of the East End, until chance led them into the Yiddish theatre. Like convalescents they felt more than usually emotional. Tears of laughter and sentiment rose to their eyes at the songs and evocations, the lively and richly pathetic tragi-comedy of the Yiddish theatre: a theatre whose Elizabethan informality, they thought, was nearer in spirit than anything in London to the theatre that Shakespeare knew. But Yiddish was doomed. In two or three generations no one would speak it any longer. Meanwhile, the vitality of its diminishing band of practitioners was unimpaired: they smacked their lips with gusto and sobbed in minor key over the expressively intimate language of the ghetto.... From the theatre to the docks; from the docks to the Embankment; from the Embankment to St. Giles; from St. Giles David and Stanley walked home long after midnight.

For the remainder of his sixth-form days, David Hirsch took little interest in determinism. Whenever the subject came up during debates or discussions with philosophically minded friends, he said: "This is where I retire. The moment determinism enters the argument I feel it has reached a profitless impasse."

He read of a lady who said to Doctor Johnson that she accepted the universe, and of Doctor Johnson's reply that she had better. Like her, David accepted the universe (while continuing to hate its tragic manifestations, to revolt against them and try to alter them) and found that he had better. He read, too, of the President who on first taking office awoke each morning gratified and surprised to find that the country had contrived to run itself overnight without his intervention. Like the President he discovered that the world ran itself without his intervention. At the same time, he was, somehow, President of his fate. The world ran itself, but from time to time, as it were, a document was brought in for him to sign and on which he had to take a decision.

A sense of universal mystery grew upon David, and while on the level of practical living he favoured a vigorous, enterprising, and humane commonsense, he wondered whether there was another reality, perhaps more real than ordinary reality. He was struck, for instance, by the unreality, according to everyday standards, of time: its strange elasticity, compressibility, and general subjectivity. And he wrote in his notebook: "Everything is as it seems. Yet there is a life underneath this life, and above it, which walks beside it, and which "resembles it like a brother". There past and present and future intermingle. There all faces which have been seen are visible, all words that have been spoken are audible, confused, yet irrevocable and unmistakable. There none grow old and all are old, none can die, and all are dead and immortal. It is the world of ourselves, the world of dreams, by day and night; the world of art, of tunes hummed, of clocks ticking, of branches shifting; of sleep, of not thinking, of walking, of passing by, and of watching...."

His reading and independent temperament had long before led him to reject the apologists of his own and other religions; now the sense of universal mystery and uncertainty led him to question also those who, sometimes with equal dogmatism and pharisaical conviction, denied and denigrated the religious mysteries. He had not ceased to believe in God, whatever that word meant; only the ideas which the word evoked had changed. Stanley objected to the word, saying that David's use of it was so private, vague, and misleading that he had far better use another. But David preferred God, which existed in all languages and among all peoples, to the Life Force, Purpose, Destiny, the First Cause, the Great Unknown; though he agreed that it was only a word, not — except insofar as words themselves somehow increase the significance of what they describe — making known the unknowable or clarifying the nebulous. If, he said, the crude and dogmatic associations of the word made it stick in his friend's throat, any other word would provisionally do.

Agnosticism led David to read again the religious books. They came to him with a freshness that would have been impossible a few generations earlier, before the rationalists had drastically cleared away the overgrowth of outdated systems, ideas, and notions, which had obscured the original works. The rationalists had, as it were, restored a series of masterpieces. The masterpieces themselves could be accepted or questioned or rejected — that was a matter for consideration — the rationalists enabled David to see the original masterpieces freshly and innocently. So when he thought of life in its broadest scope, of death and solitariness and suffering, David found himself drawing eclectically and independently on all the poetry and philosophy, all the religions and branches of religions he had ever come across. It seemed to him that the imaginative suggestions of the religious books were akin to those of poetry though they might be different in degree. As a vast series of poems they were the greatest of epics, universal and terrible; as suggestive, in their own way, as the current scientific hypotheses taught by biologists, astronomers, and geologists. For David, both poetry and science were divinely inspired. Science was provisional explicit truth, poetry was somewhat less provisional implicit truth — more could be implied, mysteriously guessed at, and glimpsed than could be stated or coherently organised. The forms, the dogmas, the intellectual systems, even the morality in which religions clothed themselves and which bore the mark of their time and place of origin were comparatively unimportant; what was important was the spirit which drove them and the poetic truths which they revealed.

4

DAVID SHARED with Stanley a harmonious friendship. This was not to say that their views were the same nor that their personalities were similar. Instead, they were able to agree on a great deal and to disagree satisfactorily on the remainder. Stanley did not in general share David's mystical tendencies. Stanley devoted his mind to equally abstruse dialectics concerned with Marxism, socialism, capitalism, fascism, and anarchism. He did not accept communism, but he accepted its phraseology and methods of reasoning; so that he found it necessary to read Marxist literature and master its algebra. David once accompanied him to an East End discussion group. The discussion had been advertised simply as "Questions and Answers", by Professor Abraham Cohen. The professor sat on a low dais facing a semi-circle of near-Marxists, mostly young men in their twenties holding large, thick tomes entitled *Dialectical Materialism, The Theory and Practice of the Social Revolution, The Labour Movement and the Dictatorship of the Proletariat.* Some listened attentively, nodded their heads, or looked up references in their stout tomes. Others took it in turns to engage the professor in a crossfire of respectful comment, question, and interpolation. The character of the discussion, the manner of the students reminded David of some previous experience. He could not at first think what. Then he remembered the Yeshivah Talmudical College. Later he found the same uncongenial atmosphere at the university or when witnessing other intellectual cults. Here Marx took the place of the Talmud, Lenin the commentary in small type, Stalin the commentary in large type, Engels the commentary at the back; the professor took the place of the rabbi, the young men the eager Talmudists, checking a reference, capping a point, displaying their dialectical virtuosity in elaborating a complicated passage to its conclusion beneath the benign, but expertly watchful eye of the mentor. The East End discussion group was a Jewish one, but there were several non-Jews present. And they, David thought, were the descendants of the catechizers, the theological hair-splitters, the doctrinal experts: all of them assiduous note-takers who had never had an idea in their heads except what was stamped into them in black and white by some dogmatic intellectual system. Then, when authority had impressed itself, their thorough, pharisaical minds proceeded to master its complicated disciplines... But the analogy, he reflected with a touch of nostalgia, was a bit hard on the Talmud, since the Talmud, properly considered, was a charming repository of ancient lore, hallowed by the studious and religious candlelight of two thousand years; whereas the latter-day Marxists represented what was graceless and oafish in scholasticism.

David Hirsch was averse not only to the Marxist meetings, but to all the local political assemblies. He told himself that he was not averse to politics itself, the substance of politics; but he was averse to listening to platitudes or lies in school halls, averse to slogans, rabble-rousing, the currying of favour, the painting of roseate dawns on the one hand, and disingenuous apologetics on the other. He would have wished politics to be a matter for sincere deliberation, fired, only when emotion was genuine, by passion. Nevertheless, he remembered that if one were to take part in politics at all, one had to deal with politics as it was and not as one would have wished it to be. The Spanish Civil War had its repercussions in Hackney and Dibley and brought together the politically-minded young people of the left in a series of precisely those meetings in school-halls and at street-corners which normally left him bored and despairfully resigned. However, the cause of Republican Spain seemed so just and urgent, and he so wanted to "do something", that on several Wednesday half-holidays he accompanied Stanley to the offices of a near-communist youth magazine in Hoxton.

The young people who assembled in a converted Hoxton shop were there in the first instance to get the magazine produced. They wrote paragraphs, roneoed sheets, clipped them, packed them on to a van. But they were naturally still more interested in talking to each other. They were a very assorted crowd: unemployed Scotsmen and Welshmen who had migrated to London, a few Hoxton and Shoreditch cockneys, several East End Jews, and a number of students. Some of the students turned out to be, like David and Stanley, still at school. David was particularly interested to meet, during the Easter holidays, two sixth-formers from Eton, who arrived in the company of a most attractive and elegant girl, the daughter of a Harley Street specialist. With the elder of the two Etonians David struck up a passing friendship. Cyril, a tall, fair-haired aristocrat, was likeable but, David thought, naively insistent on "the class war". Everywhere in England outside his own milieu, Cyril suggested, there was grinding poverty and incalculable misery resulting from it. Not only did Cyril feel guilty about his class, but he maintained that conditions in "the slums of Hackney" were his own personal fault, and still more the fault of his rich father. David and Stanley, for instance, in spite of appearances to the contrary, were probably half-starved...

David replied that he himself ate so much, so unwisely, and such enticing acidy, oily, and fatty foods that he suffered from indigestion; and that as far as Hackney was concerned, Cyril was confusing conditions now, with what they had been twenty, thirty, or fifty years before. There were poverty and misery — though even so Cyril should not exaggerate: judging from articles in the *Daily Herald,* David considered Hackney a comfortable London suburb when compared with the depressed areas of Wales, Scotland, and Northern England, let alone of countries abroad — but for the majority of people life was materially pleasant. There were slums and noisy council flats, but the majority of the houses were, at any rate externally, not so dissimilar to those in Kensington and Chelsea, Hampstead and St. John's Wood. Indeed, what had disconcerted him as a child was the fact that the disparity between Hackney and the fabulous western districts of London was rarely sufficient to be satisfying artistically. And when he came to discuss examinations with Cyril, it seemed that the education which he had received free, which he had in fact been paid to receive, was in substance, if not in spirit, the same as that which Cyril had received at Eton, the one noticeable difference being that Cyril had studied Greek, whereas at Stenholme College Greek had been dropped about ten years before. Cyril remained unconvinced, shook his head, and said: "You don't know. You just don't know what you've been missing...."

Stanley tended to support Cyril and spoke of the public-school class and the old-school tie. Fifty per cent of all Members of Parliament, he said, not merely in the Conservative and Liberal Parties, but also in the Labour Party, had been to public schools; and in other spheres of power and influence the proportion was even higher. David argued in return that it was as wrong to classify people aggressively in classes as in races. And, he added — piqued by the orthodox assumption, even though, on his own, he would have thought it just — would others, given the power and privilege of the public-school class, have behaved better or as well? He did not know, but neither did Stanley. However, he granted Stanley and Cyril that if Cyril's companions, Bereston and Sylvia, were anything to go by, the public-school class had one overriding defect: Bereston and Sylvia, even here in Hoxton, were inordinate snobs. They made a bee-line for the youth leaders from headquarters and in fact treated everyone with just the degree of consideration appropriate to his position in the hierarchy of "the movement".

The news from Spain got worse. One summer evening, walking down Mare Street, David and Stanley saw on the placards of the evening papers: "Last days of Red Madrid." The glowing ball of the sun was also red. As its broad evening light poured over the city, it seemed to David, in an unhappy fancy, that all this redness belonged to some tragic, symbolical painting; that on this summer evening the streets of the prosperous capitals of the democratic countries which had denied help to Republican Spain were flowing with blood.

Stanley voiced a thought that had crossed both their minds. "Do you think we ought to go?"

"You mean —?"

"Yes.... Perhaps."

"I don't know.... How would we set about it?"

On Sunday morning David accompanied Stanley to an office in the West End. As they were early they decided to walk from King's Cross through a district of squares which they had as yet only half explored. It was a fine day in early summer. Square succeeded square, tranquil and lovely, the gardens in full foliage, the terraces of houses lined in graceful and spacious vistas against the blue sky. Never before had London looked to them so beautiful and desirable. Why, oh why, they asked, was it not possible to enjoy the paradise that the world could be? Why these distractions, these hatreds, these wars and brutalities? Why could not men compete only in beauty and vie with each other only in magnanimity?

At the office in the West End their interview was brief. They gave a few personal details and mentioned their work for the Dibley Spain Committee. They were asked their age and replied: sixteen.

"Too young," said the secretary. "If you're to go you'll have to say you're eighteen. You could pass as eighteen at a pinch. Mind you, I'm not advising you to go, myself. You're definitely on the young side. But if you *want* to go, here are your instructions." Their instructions were to obtain passports, and when they had done so, to report back to the office for a medical examination, and then to travel to Paris, where they would join one of the contingents of volunteers that were travelling to Spain at regular intervals.

That was that. Only when they had left the office and were strolling reflectively through the peaceful Sunday streets did their doubts really begin. What were they to say to their parents? What about their school examinations? How would they fare in battle? Would they lose their nerve under fire? Getting killed wouldn't matter so much, but what if they were wounded? Meanwhile, the day was so delightful and sunny that they found it hard to believe they were faced with a grim decision. Their resolution momentarily returned when they bought a paper: the news was worse than ever, Franco's men were in the outskirts of Madrid. But they forgot it again as they walked to Regent's Park and strolled several times past H.G. Wells's house, wondering if he were having his lunch.

Turning away from Hanover Terrace, they made for the lake, deciding to get a boat out, when suddenly Stanley caught David by the arm. "Look!" he said.

"What?" asked David. Stanley was staring excitedly at an elderly man sitting on a bench and reading the Sunday paper.

"It's H.G. Wells!" exclaimed Stanley.

"No!..." But it was. There was no mistaking him; they knew his photograph too well.

"We must speak to him," said David.

"How? What can we say?"

"I know, we'll ask him for his autograph."

They walked up and down several times before plucking up the nerve to approach, cough respectfully, and stammer out a request for an autograph. H.G. Wells at first seemed a bit peeved at being disturbed. Then he smiled, and they were not disappointed. His presence was, indefinably, what they had expected. "It's a fair cop," he said with friendly jocularity. He motioned them to sit down on the bench and drew out a pen to sign the notebook which David proffered. He asked them their names and what they did. They told him and mentioned that they were wondering whether they ought to volunteer for the international brigade in Spain. Stanley added that they had seen his reply to a questionnaire sent out to authors asking for their opinion on the Spanish Civil War. The replies had been published in a pamphlet and the names of H.G. Wells and Bernard Shaw had stood at the head of the section entitled: "Neutral?" David said they respected his opinion more than anyone's, but they felt none the less that the Republican side was right both in itself and because it served the interest of the democratic nations. H.G. Wells said they should read his forthcoming book, *The Brothers,* and in it they would find the background to his views on the civil war. "Remember what I wrote at the end of my reply to the questionnaire," he said, raising a warning finger. "The real enemy of mankind is the Ignorant Fool."

"But, sir," said Stanley, "that's a long-term danger: what about here and now?... If you found a man punching your friend in the jaw, you wouldn't, surely, say that the real enemy was the Ignorant Fool on both sides?"

H.G. Wells laughed. "Well put, young man. But the world situation and the civil war aren't as simple as that, as you know. There's another danger I've written about more than once. There is an enormous surplus of energy among young people of all countries between the ages of, say, eighteen and thirty. Their demand for a cause to fight for reaches its peak between those ages, but as a rule they begin to be capable of forming anything like an independent, mature judgment only from the age of thirty onwards. Hence the legions of fascists and communists tramping belligerently through the cities of Europe with very little idea of what fascism and communism mean."

"Then you think we ought not to join the international brigade?"

H.G. Wells shook his head sadly. "I think that at the age of sixteen you are far too young to do any such thing."

Soon, with much tripping backward, apology, and confusion, David and Stanley left, their hero-worship partly appeased. H.G. Wells wished them good luck. They would have liked to believe sincerely that they were too young to take part in the world's affairs, that their youth entitled them to be spectators. But they were not able to escape a sense of responsibility. Their course, they argued, the duty which they owed less to the world than to themselves, was clear. Would they have the strength of purpose to follow it?

The day proved to be one of high drama. Not merely had they taken a step which faced them squarely with the choice either of volunteering for a cause in which they believed or of recognising their selfish insufficiency; not merely had they met H.G. Wells, but their private, poetic life was heightened by the romantic beauty of London, revealed during this summer Sunday, and by an encounter that evening in the Café Sarnuta.

After lazing about Regent's Park during the afternoon, they dropped into the Café Sarnuta on their way home. It was crowded, but while they were sipping their tea and smoking cigarettes — each had his own twopenny packet of five by this time and they had abandoned both Turkish and their homemade exotic blends for Players — they could not fail to notice a young woman with long, dark hair hanging over her shoulders staring at them fixedly from the other side of the café. She was in the company of two men, but seemed bored with their noisy back-slapping and laughter. David and Stanley were not yet accustomed to the idea that a young woman, let alone one as attractive as the dark-haired girl, might conceivably show a spontaneous interest in their raw, and as they thought, repulsive selves. A long time passed. Customers, having bought their tea at the Café Sarnuta, were in no hurry to leave. But eventually the young woman stood up and held out her hand in nonchalant and disinterested farewell to her companions. As she stepped towards the door alone, the two six-formers saw that she was indeed the last word in elegance and distinction of appearance. Before passing through the curtains into the street she turned round to look towards them with a last significant, fixed stare.

"Do you know her?" said David.

"No," said Stanley. "Do you?"

"No. I wonder who she can be."

They were not astonished, but just a little surprised, and very gratified, when a half-hour later they found her sitting on the low wall of a public garden facing the café door. They smiled uncertainly. She smiled back.

"I was wondering how much longer you'd be," she said.

"Oh, we didn't know ... but..."

"Shall we walk?"

"Yes! Yes!... Let's walk," they agreed emphatically.

They were soon strolling throught the same squares and along the same broad, still streets which they had already traversed, but in the opposite direction, that morning. Now, in the grey-blue light of early evening, the streets and squares were even more still, more sad, more romantic; and more distant from Spain.

"You were so different," said the girl. "I could see that at once. And I was fed up with those layabouts in the café."

She was an artist and took them to her studio at the top of a large house let out in rooms. She made them coffee and asked if they noticed the difference between her coffee, real coffee brewed in the continental style, and "the sort of stuff they serve over here." They replied — "All the difference in the world" — though to them all coffee tasted the same. For her part, she said, she had no time for London. Paris was the only city worth living in. She had just spent two years there and hoped soon to raise enough money to go back.... They were getting along famously when another young woman arrived, equally dark and long haired, equally attractive and distinguished, but more broody. This second girl was uninterested in David and Stanley, and even a little contemptuous. They were easily inclined to feel unwanted, and after a few awkward silences during which they very slightly but significantly raised an eyebrow to each other, they decided to go home. In any case it was growing late and the day had been long and overwhelmingly full. The first girl saw them to the door and made them promise to come to tea the following Sunday. This they promised gladly, but the invitation had a curious sequel. When they called at the studio a week later the bell was answered by a stocky and hostile landlady.

"No, she *isn't* in. Nor she's not likely to be in neither. Where is she? *You* tell *me*. If you can tell me where she is I'd be very grateful. She's gone and shot the moon."

"What does that mean?" asked David.

"I'll tell you what it means, young man. It means she's done a moonlight flit. It means she's went off in the middle of the night with all her things, leaving no address, and owing me four weeks' rent."

They looked out for her at the Café Sarnuta, but she never appeared again. Nevertheless, their encounter with her, brief though it was, had endowed that café with new possibilities. That walk through the evening streets and squares, that coffee in the Bloomsbury studio, had set a pattern, a precedent, which their romantic longings unconsciously sought to repeat.

With life so interesting and attractive in London, they could not bring themselves to do anything decisive about going to Spain. In any case, there was first of all the insuperable difficulty of getting passports. "Passports!" said their parents. "What do you want passports for?"

"To go to Spain."

"To Spain! Oy! The boys are mad! One minute you're pinning on their napkins, the next minute they're going to Spain! What do you want to go to Spain for — don't you know there's a war on there?"

"That's just it; we ought to help. Everyone ought to help. Others have gone, as young as us."

Mrs. Hirsch summed up the opinion of their families. "Pray God war doesn't come, but if it comes, it comes soon enough. You don't have to go and look for it. In any case, you're too young."

Then there were the higher school examinations and their interesting scholastic careers, with vague but hopeful future prospects. The more closely they examined the practical details of going to Spain, the less feasible did it seem to uproot themselves from the familiar ground of their school lives. No one else was going to Spain. Everyone was completely taken up with day-to-day preoccupations. Even in reading the newspapers, other people turned to the sports news, and if they could not help seeing a headline about the civil war, simply said: "Dd! Dd! ... Terrible ..." as though Spain were on another planet. In spite of their youthful individuality of judgment, David and Stanley could not help being impressed. Perhaps the Spanish Civil War was not so important after all? It would pass; it would sort itself out.

Even while they were hesitating, the news from the Republican side took a momentary turn for the better. Some newspapers and magazines spoke of new armies organising, of minor offensives the prelude to major offensives, of arms arriving in quantity from Russia and France. The more optimistic said that the tide had turned: so far Franco's side had still been benefiting from the advantages of surprise, but they had failed to pull it off, they were too late, they had lost the war ... So in an atmosphere of unexpected cheerfulness September approached, autumn drew on, another school year began, and David and Stanley, after a summer of indecision, returned to the sixth form to study for their forthcoming examination and abandoned the notion of going to Spain.

They could for the moment tell themselves that their presence was unnecessary. The Republican government itself had declared that the military situation was well in hand, and that in any case arms, not men, were needed. Nevertheless, they knew that they had failed to live up to one conception of life. And to remind them of the fact, the military situation very soon got worse, worse even than it

212

had been in midsummer. No, David thought, they had been unwilling to make the sacrifice. The poet's path had been clear and they had failed to take it ... But then, he consoled himself, remembering the little crisis which he had experienced over determinism and free will, life was not rigidly tidy, not finally arranged in logical, moral, and poetic situations. Reasonability, in the last resort, was more important than reason. To have gone to Spain would have been a noble gesture; not to have gone need not mean that he had failed himself. He had to try to do the best of which he was capable....

When war did come, David and Stanley were eighteen and they joined the air force. It seemed the most utopian of the services. They had a notion that if they were fated to die, they would like to die up in the clouds, in the future, as it were. And if H.G. Wells's stories of the future were prophetic, then it would fall to the airmen to proclaim the world state....

PART TEN
THE CARAVAN
PASSES

1

D AVID WAS very nearly the oldest boy in the school. But from an early age he was a philosopher — in the vague but not meaningless sense of the word — and he was in no hurry to leave. So long as he remained at school, the unnumbered possibilities of the future remained unnumbered, and were not reduced to one, or two, or three. Also, the longer he remained at school the more chance there was of his gaining a scholarship.

Meanwhile he led an independent and agreeable existence, without authority or responsibility, in the third year of the sixth form. He was not so much at the top of the school hierarchy, as outside it on a high level. For although he was a potential scholarship winner and in his nineteenth year, he was not a monitor or prefect, team-captain, magazine-editor, server in the tuckshop, or society chairman — except, for a short period, a member of the committee of the Literary and Philosophical Society, and once proposer of a motion at a meeting of the Debating Society. What finally debarred him from any position of real responsibility appropriate to his age and scholastic standing was his incorrigible unpunctuality. All through the school, and later, he suffered on account of this objectionable and annoying vice, until eventually some sort of allowance was made for it. It was recognised that whereas the rest of the school arrived calmly and pleasantly at five minutes to nine, he arrived panting, sweating, and guilty at five minutes past nine. In the course of time, therefore, he might have expected his unpunctuality to go unpunished, except by the discomfort and remorse he inflicted on himself. Everyone knew that he had been late in the morning since his first day at school, and that he would go on being late until his last; everyone knew and made allowance for the fact — everyone, that is, except the Steamship Yarrow.

The Steamship Yarrow (H.M.S. Yarrow, M.A. Oxon) went on putting him in detention for unpunctuality right up to the end of his stay at the school, even though he was too big to squeeze into the desks of the detention classroom, even though in other respects the Steamship conscientiously treated him as an equal. Clearly, a school prefect or society chairman could not go into detention alongside naughty boys of the third and fourth forms: hence David's independent, but unhonoured and irresponsible status in the third year of the sixth form. Not that he minded sitting in detention on Wednesday afternoons or having no prefect's badge on his cap; as a philosopher, he made the most of the one — apart from having to smash up desks in order to sit down, he could read just as well in detention as in the library — and the least of the other — any sycophant could become a prefect and was welcome to the corruption by power and the waste of time involved.

At five or ten minutes past nine every morning there occurred unfailingly a slight brush between David and the Steamship Yarrow. It was not even a brush, it was the merest glancing blow, a casual biff that the keel of the Steamship delivered as it chuffed, with broadbottomed dignity, downstream to morning prayers:

"Late again, Hirsch!"

Just that; a low, unemphatic snarl out of the corner of his mouth. The Steamship did not turn his head, he scarcely opened his lips. But his timing and aim were accurate, and the words reached David, and David alone, no matter how he sought to dodge them, shake them off, or ignore them. In his last few months at school, David did not even attempt to hurry past the Steamship, as it churned along the corridor. He strolled by peacefully, nodded to the Steamship a courteous "Good-morning, Mr. Yarrow," but received in reply the usual "Late again, Hirsch", and after a few such lates, the weekly detention ticket.

The Steamship was acting out of his overwhelming sense of duty. He was, to the eye of his pupil, a martyred piece of engineering, a mechanism for the performance of duty. Thus, duty told him to put David in detention, but duty also told him to act as man-to-man in the classroom. Very well, he acted as man-to-man, painfully and conscientiously. Duty told him to smile: he smiled, a half smile up one side of his face, sometimes a three-quarter smile. His muscles responded unwillingly, but they responded. When they got out of hand and the mechanism of duty was upset, when he really laughed — what a catastrophe! He tipped back in his chair, went crimson in the face, weird, choking sounds issued from his throat, he did not know where to look when the exhibition was over. Duty told him to have serious, understanding arguments, verging on the political, with his scholarship student, to see all points of view. Very well, he saw them; he even helped to formulate them, often with a distaste he could not conceal.

His own views were those of official England, those of, as it were, a *Times* leader writer or a constitutional historian grounded in tradition but not out of touch with modern thought. He was indeed an admirable exponent of those official views and David, without abandoning his utopianism, learnt from the Steamship to think seriously and soberly about politics and history.

The arguments which David developed under the Steamship's tuition did not supplant his utopian ideas, but ran parallel to them on a different plane. David was

216

unable to decide whether the official tradition was hypocritical or not; whether its subtleties were merely disingenuous or sprang in fact from empirical wisdom and a statesmanly profundity and involution. If hypocrisy there were, then this hypocrisy and its accompanying sense of duty had penetrated the Steamship so thoroughly that they became sincerity. The Steamship convinced himself of what he felt he ought to believe, after seeing all other points of view in the newspapers — he read six of them daily — and generally disposing of them with the official counter-arguments.

David was so impressed by the official way of looking at things, and the beautifully bound history books from which the Steamship drew his arguments, that to some extent he made them his own, and won a school prize for an essay on "Constitutional Monarchy and the Evolution of Parliamentary Democracy."

With this encouragement and evidence that he could write a good examination essay, David entered confidently for the Balliol group of history scholarships at Oxford. Not that he seriously considered his prospects of success: it just did not occur to him that he could fail. He simply had to enter for the examination, write a few essays conceived on the plane of his discussions with the Steamship Yarrow, and go through the formality of waiting for the result. And in any case, he did not care. If, owing to some absurdity, he did not go to Oxford, he would go to London, or Paris, or somewhere. So the journey to Oxford was a pleasure trip, a literary and sentimental exploration. It figured for some time afterwards, in his private dramatic catalogue, under the heading of: "When I was up at Oxford..." or, "When I was at Balliol..."

The week which he spent at Balliol College was quite as it should have been, though not memorable. Time, it has been observed, pure time, is almost impossible to recall; only when it is broken up by events, odd happenings, are we able to chart its otherwise smoothly limitless, flat spaces. David's visit to Oxford was, then, a fairly pure period of time. He saw lawns, quadrangles, towers; facades glided smoothly across his vision; they were harmonious, unbroken, during his few walks, mainly in the moonlight, by those distinctive and discordant knobs and projections to which memory clings.

Instead he had a vague and agreeable impression of clean white mist, of soft perspective in grey, old but fresh: a gentle and lovely city, if he ignored that portion of it which was very similar to the suburbs of other towns.

A few happenings, however, a few deviations from absolute normalcy and harmony, unnecessary to the pure functioning of time, but indispensable footholds and handholds to the process of recollection — a few of these, what the reader may now feel to be accursed things, whatever they are, did actually form part of his brief stay at Oxford.

First, the call of the "bedder" at seven o'clock in the morning: not just a tap at the door and an announcement that it was time to get up, but a little song chanted deferentially through the keyhole:

"Seven o'clock in the morning, Sir!
Seven o'clock on a lovely morning, Sir!
Seven o'clock br-ight and early i-in the morning, Sir!"

An old Oxford tradition, David presumed.

Then there was the scholarship interview which he was summoned to attend in the room of one of the college elders; a sort of general intelligence and personality test in which he expected to make up for any deficiences in factual knowledge that he might just conceivably have inadvertently appeared to show in the written paper. He was ready for anything, the most recondite, the most esoteric, the most subtle of discussions. David arrived at the elder's room scarcely five minutes late and found it crammed and strewn, in dim and agreeable untidiness,

218

with books, desks, cushions, lamps, pens, files, and type-writers. In a clearing by the fireplace, lit by a single weak reading lamp, the not-so-old college elder, contorted in an armchair, slumped in appalling weariness and despair. He seemed really done in. His head lay so heavily on his fist that his face was pushed into a fantastic shape. But the voice which issued from his lips twisted by a row of knuckles was cheerful, even chirpy.

"Hiya!" he said, or maybe just "Hi!" or "Hm!"

One of his long legs rested, like a piece of loose scaffolding, across the other. His trousers were in any case excessively short, and the way he sat had hitched them up almost to expose the knee. This caused David to notice something curious; the college elder was wearing on one of his legs an ordinary man's sock, and on the other a pink silk stocking. David could conceive of no explanation of this fact, nor could he later offer any comment on it; nor on the other hand could he agree to its being questioned or denied. He simply knew that it had been so: a silk stocking on the right leg.

David felt that he and this don would immediately come to an understanding, would sense that they spoke the same language; and that simply in recognition of this fact, without having to put himself out, he would be recommended for the scholarship. He was prepared to be unemphatically brilliant and profound about anything: say, French poetry, or the future of mankind, or crime. He waited with real curiosity to see what the don's first question would be.

"What do you think," said the don, "of the new Hackney Town Hall?"

The question was legitimate, but unexpected. David was knocked off his balance and did not properly recover it for the remainder of the interview. As a serious conversationalist he was either good or very bad. If he was disconcerted he had a tendency to ramble gaily and incoherently. This was now the case. David mumbled something about having noticed that they had knocked down the old one. He had heard that they were building a new town hall somewhere round the back and he had, in fact, once taken a peek at it through a gap in the hoarding. Yes, it looked all right. The stone was bright and clean, but he supposed that before long the London smoke would turn it grey. The old Town Hall had its interest, when one was used to it. It beetled over Mare Street, all turrets and battlements and buttresses and squat, massive stone-work, prepared to withstand any siege by the unemployed or the communists, who held their Friday night rallies beside the buttresses of one of the banqueting halls. Practically all the rooms at the front of this former building were banqueting halls, through whose solidly defended windows one glimpsed the red necks and pink faces of the local rotarians, freemasons, conservatives, and liberals at their banqueting and toasting.

"To our old friend and former president, Mr. Humphreys, a credit to Hackney!" floated through the window, followed by a loud mooing of approval and the clinking of glasses.

"To Mr. Richardson, George to all of us, a staunch and *generous* supporter..." Moooo! For he's a jolly good fellow! On some evenings the outside of the Town Hall was positively like that of a restaurant, with its arrows and notices and directions: "To the Banqueting Hall" — "To the Rotarians' Dinner" — "To the Liberal Party Reunion and Supper" — "To the Buffet".

All this David related to the weary don, who listened gravely and impassively.

But there was an even older town hall in Hackney, David continued, long out of use as a municipal headquarters and occupied by a branch of the Midland Bank — his own bank, incidentally, David added, and very accommodating they were, too, in the matter of overdrafts. He drew his grant through the old town hall branch and they were usually willing to advance it some weeks before it was due to arrive. They called such an overdraft "accommodation", as though they were an hotel. "We are able to grant you

220

accommodation for six weeks as requested." Still, a good bank, the Midland, he would never change ... that, in effect, was what he thought of the new Hackney town hall.... Shortly after David's return from Oxford, the hoardings were removed and the new town hall was revealed — behind a little garden which grew on the site of the banqueting halls where the Rotarians used to make merry — as an adequate and pleasing modern building, perhaps the most agreeable in Hackney.

The interview ended inconclusively and — to anticipate — David failed to get his scholarship. However, it does not follow that his rambling remarks about the Hackney Town Halls were responsible. The fact was that he had not taken the written papers, either, with the seriousness necessary for success. He wrote a little, he dreamed, he looked around at the other candidates scribbling for dear life, he yawned, wrote a little more, dozed off for a bit. After all, he was a philosopher....

The final ripple on the pure, smooth flow of time at Oxford was provided by a fellow scholarship competitor of Finnish origin who rejoiced — that was the only word for it — in the name of Gottabum. Gottabum had the most extensive and accurate knowledge of genuine contemporary folk-song and poetry that David ever came across, though in bar and barrack-room he later met innumerable other fervid and prodigious enthusiasts for the genre. Ivor Gottabum clinched the certainty of David's failing to secure a scholarship — he, Gottabum, did not fail, but sneaked in at Jesus! — by keeping David up throughout the last three nights with a bottle of whisky and an uninterrupted flow of contemporary folk epics, beginning, of course, with "The Good Ship Venus" and "Eskimo Nell". (David eventually came to the conclusion that this was the only sort of spontaneous and vital folk-poetry likely to be produced this side of utopia.)

After his attempt at Oxford, David sat for one or two other scholarships; but where, before, the thought of failing did not enter his mind, now, the thought of success was totally absent. One scholarship for which he entered en passant and then forgot about, was the modern language travelling scholarship for study abroad. The examination was entirely oral, and since he spoke French well, David did after all gain a scholarship. Moreover, as successes, like failures, were strongly attracted to one another, he gained two other little scholarships as well. By passing the Intermediate Arts examination the previous year, he had already secured the usual exhibition which paid for three years' fees at London University. These two little scholarships ensured that he would also have funds to support him when, on his return from France, he began to study modern languages, as he had decided to do, at University College.

However, the problematical and supererogatory future after his return from France did not greatly concern him, although it was convenient to have it safely wrapped up and out of the way. What did concern him was the choice of the district in Paris in which he should live, and the question of whether he should afterwards go on to Brittany, the Pyrenees, or the Riviera. The terms and funds of the scholarship gave him freedom to go where he pleased, provided he made arrangements to perfect his French. He chose Auteuil in Paris and Cannes on the Riviera.

2

AVID'S last evening in London before going abroad received a certain amount of publicity. He went, with several of his friends, to a party in the basement room in Charlotte Street of Mr. Ruthercliffe Crowne, an acquaintance from the Bohemia of St. Giles. The room was full of orange boxes and straw and a spreading, indeterminate pile of old blankets which passed for the bed. David and his friends were invited, or rather ordered in a friendly way, to read the wall magazine *Sheauough* (pronounced "Shoo"). It gave highly informed details of the scandals of Fitzrovia. Having read it, they had their attention drawn, by the black-bearded, messianic-looking Mr. Ruthercliffe Crowne, to a broken saucer underneath *Sheauough,* beside which was a notice saying:

"One penny please."

They dropped in their pennies.

"Have some tea," said Mr. Ruthercliffe Crowne.

"Er ... no thanks," they said, not too happy about either the ingredients or the crockery, which lay in the ruins of a fireplace.

"No, but really!"

"All right. Thanks."

The tea came up, and after it another broken saucer bearing the notice:

"Give according to your means."

Some sort of record was then put on what was approximately a gramophone, and an inhabitant of one of the upstairs rooms, a Cingalese poet, went through a series of movements which Mr. Ruthercliffe Crowne described as "dancing to Cingalese music". Needless to say, after this performance, a third broken saucer made an appearance. These saucers, they found, were designed for mugs; because when the gang came in — about six hundred Bohemians from the Café Sarnuta — they disappeared.

The gang had arrived in response to a rumour that the *Picture Journal* was going to photograph Mr. Ruthercliffe Crowne's basement for an article on London's Bohemia. The ruined cellar was filled to suffocation. David and his friends had not heard of the rumour before coming to tea, but after re-knotting their ties to treble thickness, ruffling their hair, and being pushed by the mêlée among some very beautiful negresses, they too were ready. Cigarette smoke billowed across the room; the so-called

223

Cingalese record, played again and again, was just weirdly audible above the terrific din; David leaned across one of the negresses to speak to his friends when — flash! — the first picture had been taken. Flash! Flash! Another two photographs and it was all over ... Half a page of the article, when it appeared, was taken up by a photograph of David headed: "Young painter lies unconventionally in the lap of his negress model".

Late that night, outside the Whitfield Mission in Tottenham Court Road, David stood with Stanley, Tony, and Uncle Jake —

"dear friends of other times"

— looked around at the silent, forsaken streets, and experienced the full, melancholy significance of such moments of parting. In the empty streets there was for him the sadness of school corridors at the end of term. All that had caught him up in its vitality and immediacy was seen to be impermanent and now abandoned.

But it was in an opposite, unregretful mood that he contemplated the implacable onrush of life and change on the following morning of glittering sunshine. The bus moved up Piccadilly: from the roadway, light flashed on chromium and glass, criss-crossed beneath the blue sky, reflected long rays from the grey buildings on the one side to the variegated green of the park on the other. With his mother and young brother to see him off, he entered the cavern of Victoria Station, anteroom to Europe. He stood up to the very last moment on the platform speaking of luggage and postcards, toothbrushes and tickets, and watching the great engine that waited, patiently and powerfully, for the signal to perform its labour.

The whistle blew, he kissed his mother and brother, and still watched the engine and the outer steel rods and shafts and axles which began slowly to function. He was awed and intoxicated by their overwhelming force; they became momentarily symbolical of the whole irresistible power of life and perpetual change, of which all men were part, which must crush them all, and which yet gave them new forms and, even in corruption unto death, new life. The train was already moving when he jumped into the carriage and took his seat. The spectacle of that colossal engine gently, irresistibly, and implacably revolving and thrusting its weighty metal limbs in an ever-faster rhythm, transformed itself, as he leaned back and closed his eyes, into a rhetorical, verbal music. For their sonority, in the first place, rather than for any significance which might be given to them, three words repeated themselves in his mind. They were the title of a book that he had come across in the course of his early studies of Spanish: *La Caravana Pasa* — *The Caravan Passes*. That was what the engine seemed to be saying, again and again, with gathering speed, then steadily and with peaceful monotony .... La caravana pasa, la caravana pasa, la caravana pasa ... la caravana pasa, la caravana pasa ... la caravana pasa ... la caravana pasa ... la caravana pasa ... Pass on, mighty caravan!

NEW LONDON EDITIONS

Available

King Dido by *Alexander Baron*
(introduction by *Ken Worpole*)

Scamp by *Roland Camberton*
(introduction by *Iain Sinclair*)

Rosie Hogarth by *Alexander Baron*
(introduction by *Andrew Whitehead*)

Forthcoming

Adrift in Soho by *Colin Wilson*

The Furnished Room by *Laura Del-Rivo*

This Bed My Centre by *Pamela Hansford Johnson*
(introduction by *Zoë Fairbairns*)

October Day by *Frank Griffin*
(introduction by *Andy Croft*)

Available from bookshops or www.fiveleaves.co.uk